SCIENCE AND LANGUAGE

USES OF ENGLISH

A Series for College Composition

THOMAS W. WILCOX, General Editor

USES OF ENGLISH

SCIENCE
AND LANGUAGE

Selected Essays

Edited by

ALFRED M. BORK
REED COLLEGE

D. C. HEATH AND COMPANY BOSTON

D. C. HEATH AND COMPANY

Boston Englewood Chicago San Francisco Atlanta Dallas London Toronto

Contents

Introduction

The expression "language of science," as used in some contemporary journalism, may seem little more than a turn of speech. But the authors in this collection would probably agree in finding this a useful expression of the fact that scientific patterns of thought, communicated in terms of scientific materials, form a distinctive communicating system that deserves the name of language structure. Because a system for communicating scientific concepts has its own special problems, its functions as a language may have an unusual relationship to those of the language of everyday speech.

The essays may help students explore the ways in which our verbal assumptions can affect scientific work, or the ways in which scientific arguments may be mustered in the arena of verbal persuasion; they do not deal concretely with the problems of expressing scientific knowledge in language structures. Nevertheless, students would do well to keep in mind that issues between the concerns of language and of science have practical implications that are already worked out in a great variety of "languages of science" now in use for purposes of study and communication of research.

Some scientific languages are only slight modifications of everyday languages like English; the only addition may be a specialized vocabulary or a vocabulary which modifies and makes more precise the meaning of certain words. But in the physical sciences the languages of science are more nearly like languages in their own right, less dependent on any natural language; they employ their own symbols, usually mathematical or logical symbols, as "words" which are not contained in the ordinary verbal language.

These highly symbolic scientific languages serve the purposes of communication much as any language system does, though the linguistic units are almost entirely written or graphic, and so are much removed from the oral basis of spoken language systems. The most abstract and symbolic of these languages still has its own strict system of grammatical construction; not every combination of scientific symbols forms an allowable sentence in the scientific language, just as not every collection of English words forms an allowable English sentence. If one takes the three symbols "2", "3" and "=" these symbols cannot be written down in just any order. The ordering "23=" or "=23" are orderings that violate the grammatical rules of the language, but the ordering "2 = 3" is allowed in the language. Thus, as in any linguistic system, usage of grammatical rules is completely independent of questions of truth. Furthermore, the dependence of a scientific or mathematical grammar on the linguistic features of an Indo-European verb system (as in the use of an equals sign for a "to be" verb in "$2 = 3$") may be superseded in an almost independent grammar, as in a sophisticated mathematical sentence. To some degree all the following essays explore the problem of the dependence or independence of scientific knowledge to the language systems available to express it.

These essays are not selected or arranged according to any special thesis of calculated plan of sequential development; each was chosen for its intrinsic interest and penetrating analysis of the relationship between the concerns of science and of language. All the essays show a close interaction between style and idea; some are popularizations of particular areas of science, some are from literature for scientists, and some are from literature about science, history and philosophy of science. The chronological spread is from the Victorian, W. K. Clifford, to the present. The principal organizing theme is an examination of issues that underlie a language of science.

SCIENCE AND LANGUAGE

Science and Language

PHILIPP G. FRANK

Contemporary Science and the Contemporary World View

Philipp Frank is a physicist and philosopher of science. He was a member of the "Vienna Circle," a group of philosophers who developed the position known as logical positivism. He was Professor of Theoretical Physics at Prague before coming to Harvard University.

From some quarters the suggestion has been made to stop research in science for a time, because it threatens to bring about eventually the destruction of mankind. One is told one should rather devote more effort to work in the field of the humanities. The hope is that in this way ethics and religion will develop to a level at which they are able to adapt the human mind to the threat of contemporary science. There are, of course, old myths according to which mankind was once forced to a moratorium on scientific research. Chapter eleven in Genesis tells us that the children of men had made great advances in mechanical engineering. By introducing brick and mortar construction they built a great city. "And the Lord came down to see the city and the tower, which the children of men builded And the Lord said 'Behold, they are one people, and they have all one language; and this is what they begin to do: and now nothing will be withholden from them, which they purpose to do. Come, let us go down, and there confound their language, that they may not understand one another's speech.' So the Lord scattered them abroad from thence upon the face of all the earth: and they left off building the city." Scientific research had to stop for a time and the children of Adam had to turn to the humanities: they had to study languages.

P. Frank. "Contemporary Science and the Contemporary World View." *Daedalus*, winter 1958, 57–66. Reprinted by permission from *Daedalus*, published by the American Academy of Arts and Sciences. Also by permission of Beacon Press.

We can learn from this biblical story that there has been an old tradition according to which exaggerated scientific and technological advance is dangerous for mankind and a direct intervention of God had to produce a moratorium on research. In our century the work in science has evidently recovered so well that we now can hear quite a few voices calling for a new Babylonic confusion.

It has been said again and again that there is an exaggerated emphasis on science in our educational system which produces undesirable effects in the personalities of our students. Many educators — and every grownup claims to be an educator — have made the point that the neglect of the humanistic studies is responsible for the general decline in spiritual values and, perhaps, in human values in general. The mind of educators manifests itself in the most conspicuous way in commencement speeches, and there we frequently hear the assertion that this state of affairs leads to an emphasis on "facts" at the cost of values.

However, a poet and humanist like Archibald MacLeish regards this objection as superficial. His own objection to science as the main topic of education is rather that science deals too little with facts and concentrates on abstractions. "This sort of thing has consequences," writes MacLeish in the *Atlantic Monthly* (March, 1956). "Abstractions have a limiting, a dehumanizing, a dehydrating effect on the relation to things of the man who must live with them. The result is that we are more and more left, in our scientific society, without the means of knowledge of ourselves as we truly are or of our experience as it actually is." According to MacLeish, science gives us only abstractions of the world; we do not learn what our world really *is*. "Science can abstract ideas about apples from apples . . . but poetry does not abstract. Poetry presents the thing as the thing . . . the true child of abstraction can't know apple as apple . . . you can't know man as man. All you can *know* is a world dissolved by analyzing intellect into abstraction — not a world composed by imaginative intellect into itself."

We can find similar ideas in the discussion by literary men of the difference between the general world picture of the sciences and the humanities. Thus Aldous Huxley writes in his little book *Science, Liberty and Peace* (New York, 1946), that the scientists and their followers tend to accept the world picture which is implicit in the theories of science as a complete and exhaustive account of reality. Huxley insists that "the scientific picture of the world is inadequate for the simple reason that science does not even profess to deal with experience as a whole, but only with certain aspects of it in certain contexts." He contrasts the few abstractions of which science consists with "the infinitely rich totality of given facts." For these reasons, students who are brought up in merely scientific thinking will know only a poor and dry, geometrical and mechanical skeleton of the world. They will feel helpless if exposed to the full reality of the world.

Other authors, viewing science as a dehumanized abstraction, conclude that science cannot have any influence on philosophy as a world view which determines our way of life. Evidently this guidance should be left completely to irrational sources of knowledge, for example religion, metaphysics and, implicitly, political philosophy. But, in fact, this "dehumanizing" and "dehydrating" influence of science has had at all times an important impact upon man's ideas of his place in the universe and, therefore, upon his general philosophy of life. This impact is established by empirical observation with the same certainty as any empirical fact of human or natural history. The ancient conflict between Epicurean materialism and Platonic idealism had its basis in the scientific conflict between the hypothesis that the earth and celestial bodies (sun and stars) are all made of the same material and the ancient belief that terrestrial and celestial materials are fundamentally different. Newton established a theory of the universe according to which the celestial bodies (including comets) move by the same laws as stones and projectiles that are launched by man; and the Newtonian philosophy was the basis of Jefferson's democratic ideas. In our century, the theory of relativity has been interpreted frequently as favoring idealistic philosophy because physics no longer speaks about the "real length of a body" but about its "length for an individual observer." This is taken to mean that physical science deals with mental phenomena instead of with material objects. In a similar way, in quantum theory the physicist does not describe the objective position or the objective orbits of particles, but the measurements made by observers under certain circumstances. Both theories seem to oppose the mechanistic and materialistic philosophies of the eighteenth and nineteenth centuries and to favor a mentalistic picture of the world.

As a matter of fact, the view that science is the product of abstraction from our rich and full experience is rather misleading. It has become more and more clear by the evolution of science in our century that the principles of science are not dehydrated abstractions but a system of symbols that is produced by the creative imagination of the scientist. This has been nowhere demonstrated as clearly as in Einstein's Herbert Spencer Lectures (given at Oxford, 1933) on the Logical Foundations of Theoretical Physics. There is no process of abstraction by which we can proceed from our experience with moving bodies to Newton's laws of motion or to Einstein's equations of motion in a gravitational field as they are advanced by the general theory of relatively. While our experiences of motion can be described in common-sense language, the general principles (like Newton's or Einstein's laws of motion) contain symbols like "curved four-dimensional space" or "length relative to a system F" which do not belong to the common-sense language which we use for the description of our daily life experience. In the same way, the principles of quantum theory contain words like "probability of a particle to be at a certain place" or "ψ-function of a certain field of force" which are not to be found in our common-sense language.

The connection between the general principles (like the equations of motion in the general theory of relativity) and the common-sense level consists in the following: from the general principles we can derive, by long mathematical chains, statements which describe directly observable facts and which can, therefore, be formulated in a common-sense language. Einstein stresses the point that the advance in science is connected with an increasing remoteness of the general principles from statements of our common-sense language. As a matter of fact, even the statements of Newtonian physics cannot really be formulated in common-sense language, but in the relativity and quantum theories the impossibility becomes obvious.

The more remote the language of the principles is from common-sense language, the longer becomes the mathematical chain that connects these principles with the statements which describe the actually observable phenomena by which the theory is checked. Sometimes the chains are without precise end. We must not forget that these chains do not consist of mathematical deductions only. We would never arrive at a statement that could be checked by actual physical operations unless the chain contained at some place operational definitions by which a connection between the symbols at the top and the measurements at the bottom was established. In theories like the quantum theory, the presentation of operational definitions becomes a difficult and controversial task.

One cannot wonder that there has always been an urge to connect the principles with common-sense language by some shorter and more direct way. There has been a longing to restore the situation in which the general principles themselves are congruent to common sense. Today we have the impression that Aristotelian and Thomistic physics had this property. The attempts to give direct common-sense interpretation to the principles of relativity theory and quantum theory have played a considerable role in our time. Thus the expression "length relative to a certain system of reference" has frequently been replaced by "length relative to an individual observer" who was even occasionally referred to as "Peter" or "Paul." According to the theory of relativity there is an influence of motion upon yardsticks. Hence, every description of a length measurement has to contain the speed of the yardstick. But by referring to "length" as the sense impression of "Peter" or "Paul" the dependence of length upon the system of reference becomes a dependence upon the mental state of "Peter" or "Paul." This is the short circuit by which the expression "length with respect to a system of reference" becomes an expression of common-sense language; but now it asserts that there is an influence of optical sensation upon the mental state of "Peter or "Paul." As soon as we replace the expressions that occur in the theory of relativity by these anthropomorphic common-sense terms, the physical theory becomes a kind of psychological theory. From this common-sense interpretation the result is derived that physics actually speaks about the mental phenomena of individuals. Then it is quite natural to interpret modern science in favor of an idealistic or skeptical world view and to deny that science can provide knowledge about physical reality. In a similar way, in quantum theory, the impossibility of introducing position and velocity of a particle at a certain instant of time as state variables has also been interpreted by statements in common-sense language — by a "short circuit," without the long chain that leads to observable phenomena. In one such interpretation the position and velocity of a particle at the same instant of time are said to be inaccessible to the research abilities of human beings, and according to another interpretation, these quantities are actually not strictly determined but vague. If we use the common-sense meaning of the terms employed, this can only mean that the world itself is something vague and can be investigated, not by the methods of science, which are striving for precise and logical results, but by methods used in investigating the "irrational" and "spontaneous" aspects of the world: by metaphysics, religion, mysticism. So some have seen in modern physics a possibility of reconciling science with religion and metaphysics.

From the scientific viewpoint it is impossible to interpret the principles of quantum theory in common-sense language, except by deriving from them observable conclusions; "short circuits" between the principles of quantum theory or relativity theory and common-sense language are within scientific discourse, strictly speaking, impossible. Regardless of how great the effort in this direction is, the results achieved are always vague and, to a high degree, arbitrary. This means, of course, only that they are "logically arbitrary"; they cannot be derived with certainty by logical operations. But "arbitrary" does not mean that these common-sense interpretations are the result of our "free choice." The choice is, as a matter of fact, determined by our "values," and our predilection for a certain philosophy of life, since different common-sense interpretations could and would support different philosophies of life.

A familiar example is given by the Einstein theory, according to which a mass can be "converted" into an energy. This conversion of mass is, in the common-sense language, a "disappearance" of mass or a "dematerialization," and it would imply not physics but magic and the occult. In advancing the theory, the physicist does not use "mass" as a word of the common-sense language. If forced to introduce common-sense language, he would have to say either that energy is mass and one kind of mass is converted into another kind of mass, or else that mass is basically energy and that there is no "mass" in the common-sense meaning of the word. The first interpretation would favor materialism, the second idealism or spiritualism. Contemporary Soviet philosophers have frequently written in favor of the first interpretation, holding that the other would be antagonistic to the political philosophy supported by the government and the ruling party. In the opposite camp, many attempts to "refute materialism" have invoked the second interpretation, which abolished matter.

The introduction of common-sense language where it does not belong has also played a role in domains far removed from physics. If we introduce into theology expressions like "almightiness of God," or "goodness of God," they lead certainly to contradictions, just as the introduction of "position and velocity of a particle at the same moment" leads to contradictions in atomic physics. Obviously all such expressions denoting qualities of God are terms of our common-sense language. To avoid such terms in theology the notion of a "God without qualities" has been introduced — an example of the attempt to cast the principles of theology in a language other than our common-sense language. But this so-called "negative theology" and other such doctrines always have to fight against infiltration by common-sense expressions; and hitherto no language has found the general acceptance in theology as, for example, the symbolism of quantum theory has in physics.

If we want to understand the impact of twentieth-century science upon man's general world picture, we have to consider the popular assertion or hope that twentieth-century science may be easier to reconcile with religion and ethics than was the case in the eighteenth or nineteenth century. As a matter of fact, all these attempts at reconciliation have been attempts to produce a short circuit from science to theology analogous to the attempted short circuit from the principles of quantum theory to indeterminism and free will. Briefly, the hope for reconciliation has not been based upon science, but upon the vague interpretations of scientific principles by the introduction of common-sense language.

The British philosopher Broad wrote once that there has been only one plausible argument for supporting traditional religion by science: the existence of scientific laws which are "simple" compared with the immense multitude of "facts" that can be derived from them. A priori, it is not self-evident or even plausible that such laws should exist; but science has found that they do exist. The belief that nature is ruled in every respect by a few such laws is the content of what Einstein called "cosmic religion." But Einstein always maintained that for this argument it does not make any difference whether those laws are Newton's laws of mechanics or the laws of relativistic physics or the laws of quantum theory provided that these laws are helpful in comprehending nature by permitting the derivation of a multitude of facts from simple principles. Whatever the laws are, they give, in this parlance, testimony of God's presence in the universe.

I believe that the advances in philosophy which have been stimulated by twentieth-century physics, like relativity and quantum theory, are not advances in metaphysics but advances in semantics. Twentieth-century science has taught us that the fundamental vocabulary for formulating the principles of science can and may have to be very different from our common-sense language, and that, as a consequence, a long chain of difficult arguments is necessary in order to draw testable conclusions from these general principles.

We learn from twentieth-century science that the main advances of science depend not only on the discovery of new facts but on the invention of a new language that can connect these facts with simple principles. We remember the scriptural admonition "Do not pour new wine in old bottles." Einstein used to say that what interested him in the liberation of nuclear energy was not its military or peaceful utilizations but the fact that the fundamental law for these energy-liberating reactions can be logically derived from the principle of relativity. In the same vein, P. W. Bridgman pointed out in the essay "The Prospect for Intelligence" (Yale Review, 1945), that the impact of twentieth-century physics upon human values is twofold. Firstly, the new discoveries in the realm of very small and very large distances and masses have certainly had a great influence upon man's estimation of his position in the universe. "However," writes Bridgman, "the second aspect of the modern epoch in science is, I believe, of incomparably greater significance. The new facts have proved to be so deeply at variance with what had been conceived to be the possible order of nature that the physicist has had to dig down into an analysis of the fundamental tenets of thinking, and has to revise his entire conceptual structure."

This revision, required by the circumstance that the vocabulary used in the principles of science is so remote from out common-sense language, is apparent on reading almost any book on the general principles of quantum theory. Long passages are devoted to clearing up the relations between the technological expressions and our common-sense language. For example, in quantum theory the term "particle" is employed as a thing which has no precise position and velocity, and so is clearly incompatible with the full common-sense meaning of this word. I once asked Niels Bohr whether it would not be practical to eliminate the term "particle" completely from quantum theory. Bohr agreed that one could do so in the interest of unambiguity. But our intuitive thinking in mechanics is strongly tied to the concept of a particle. What we use in quantum theory has some properties of the common-sense particle, but not all of them. As a conceptual tool this "quasi-particle" is helpful because we can use some of our common-sense judgements about its motion; it is stimulating for the thinking of the physicist, particularly the experimental physicist.

This is why the concept remains in the theory, despite its patent dangers. Bridgman rightly makes the point that in our discourse on religion, politics or ethics, we are speaking continually in terms which we may or may not be using in their common-sense meaning. There is no doubt that political or religious discourse on general questions uses freely terms like "freedom," "democracy," "well-being of the community," etc., which are not actually to be taken in their common-sense meaning. Bridgman thinks that a clear separation between the different levels of meaning in our political or religious discourse would destroy much of the misunderstanding which makes human relations difficult. What we can learn from contemporary science for our general world view is the technique of analyzing the meaning of terms. This analysis is inseparable from doctrines like quantum theory. Without a precise formulation of the operational meaning of terms it would be impossible to draw conclusions from these principles about observable facts. Specifically, Bridgman has stressed that the application of this technique would reveal a great many questions put by philosophy and theology to be as meaningless as speculations concerning the absolute speed of the earth or the precise position and momentum of a particle.

At the end, I return to the assertion of MacLeish that science gives only abstractions while poetry presents "reality." This distinction is well analyzed by Richard von Mises in his book, *Positivism, an Essay in Human Understanding* (Harvard University Press, 1951). We have seen that the main activity of science does not consist in producing abstractions from experience. It consists in the invention of symbols and in the building of a symbolic system from which our experience can be logically derived. This system is the work of creative imagination which acts on the basis of our experience. The work of the scientist is probably not fundamentally different from the work of the poet. "Reality in its fullness" can be grasped neither by the scientist nor by the poet. Reality can only be experienced, never presented; we cannot even know what it would mean to present "reality." Every presentation, scientific or poetic, proceeds by creating symbols. If we ask which of them comes closer to reality, we employ the word "reality" again in a twilight region where it is not clear whether the word is used in its common-sense meaning or not. If somebody would claim to present the "full reality," I would question modestly, "Really?"

I sense that some people may say: "You have spoken only about words; we should prefer to hear about facts." However, science and all other types of knowledge, including art, consist in building up systems of symbols; words are merely one kind of symbol. Non-scientists often believe that science consists in making observations, in accumulating experience. But this image misses the point. At every moment of our life we perceive data of experience, yet by recording them we do not get science. Science begins only when we invent a system of symbols which can bring order into our experience. For building up science, the creation of words and their syntax is as important as experiments. A part of our science is contained in the vocabulary and the syntax of the English, French or German that we use. And this is a province of the philosophy of science; for, as L. Wittgenstein put it in the book *Philosophical Investigations* (London, 1954): "One might give the name 'philosophy' to what is possible *before* all new discoveries and inventions."

RICHARD P. FEYNMAN

Scientific Imagination

Richard P. Feynman is an outstanding contemporary theoretical physicist. Several years ago he was persuaded to teach the two year beginning physics course at the California Institute of Technology, and this passage occurs in the resulting textbook.

I have asked you to imagine these electric and magnetic fields. What do you do? Do you know how? How do *I* imagine the electric and magnetic field? What do *I* actually see? What are the demands of scientific imagination? Is it any different from trying to imagine that the room is full of invisible angels? No, it is not like imagining invisible angels. It requires a much higher degree of imagination to understand the electromagnetic field than to understand invisible angels. Why? Because to make invisible angels understandable, all I have to do is to alter their properties *a little bit* — I make them slightly visible, and then I can see the shapes of their wings, and bodies, and halos. Once I succeed in imagining a visible angel, the abstraction required — which is to take almost invisible angels and imagine them completely invisible — is relatively easy. So you say, "Professor, please give me an approximate description of the electromagnetic waves, even though it may be slightly inaccurate, so that I too can see them as well as I can see almost invisible angels. Then I will modify the picture to the necessary abstraction."

R. P. Feynman, R. B. Leighton, M. Sands. *The Feynman Lectures on Physics.* (Addison-Wesley, Reading, 1964) Volume II, Chapter 20. Reprinted by permission of the California Institute of Technology, © California Institute of Technology, 1964.

I'm sorry I can't do that for you. I don't know how. I have no picture of this electromagnetic field that is in any sense accurate. I have known about the electromagnetic field a long time — I was in the same position 25 years ago that you are now, and I have had 25 years more of experience thinking about these wiggling waves. When I start describing the magnetic field moving through space, I speak of the E- and B- fields and wave my arms and you may imagine that I can see them. I'll tell you what I see. I see some kind of vague shadowy, wiggling lines — here and there is an E and B written on them somehow, and perhaps some of the lines have arrows on them — an arrow here or there which disappears when I look too closely at it. When I talk about the fields swishing through space, I have a terrible confusion between the symbols I use to describe the objects and the objects themselves. I cannot really make a picture that is even nearly like the true waves. So if you have some difficulty in making such a picture, you should not be worried that your difficulty is unusual.

Our science makes terrific demands on the imagination. The degree of imagination that is required is much more extreme than that required for some of the ancient ideas. The modern ideas are much harder to imagine. We use a lot of tools, though. We use mathematical equations and rules, and make a lot of pictures. What I realize now is that when I talk about the electromagnetic field in space, I see some kind of a superposition of all of the diagrams which I've ever seen drawn about them. I don't see little bundles of field lines running about because it worries me that if I ran at a different speed the bundles would disappear. I don't even always see the electric and magnetic fields because sometimes I think I should have made a picture with the vector potential and the scalar potential, for those were perhaps the more physically significant things that were wiggling.

Perhaps the only hope, you say, is to take a mathematical view. Now what is a mathematical view? From a mathematical view, there is an electric field vector and a magnetic field vector at every point in space; that is, there are six numbers associated with every point. Can you imagine six numbers associated with each point in space? That's too hard. Can you imagine even *one* number associated with every point? I cannot! I can imagine such a thing as the temperature at every point in space. That seems to be understandable. There is a hotness and coldness that varies from place to place. But I honestly do not understand the idea of a *number* at every point.

So perhaps we should put the question: Can we represent the electric field by something more like a temperature, say like the displacement of a piece of jello? Suppose that we were to begin by imagining that the world was filled with thin jello and that the fields represented some distortion — say a stretching or twisting — of the jello. Then we could visualize the field. After we "see" what it is like we could abstract the jello away. For many years that's what people tried to do. Maxwell, Ampere, Faraday, and others tried to understand electromagnetism this way. (Sometimes they called the abstract jello "ether.") But it turned out that the attempt to imagine the electromagnetic field in that way was really standing in the way of progress. We are unfortunately limited to abstractions, to using instruments to detect the field, to using mathematical symbols to describe the field, etc. But nevertheless, in some sense the fields are real, because after we are all finished fiddling around with mathematical equations — with or without making pictures and drawings or trying to visualize the thing — we can still make the instruments detect the signals from Mariner II and find out about galaxies a billion miles away, and so on.

The whole question of imagination in science is often misunderstood by people in other disciplines. They try to test our imagination in the following way. They say, "Here is a picture of some people in a situation. What do you imagine will happen next?" When we say, "I can't imagine," they may think we have a weak imagination. They overlook the fact that whatever we are *allowed* to imagine in science must be *consistent with everything else we know:* that the electric fields and the waves we talk about are not just some happy thoughts which we are free to make as we wish, but ideas which must be consistent with all the laws of physics we know. We can't allow ourselves to seriously imagine things which are obviously in contradiction to the known laws of nature. And so our kind of imagination is quite a difficult game. One has to have the imagination to think of something that has never been seen before, never been heard of before. At the same time the thoughts are restricted in a strait jacket, so to speak, limited by the conditions that come from our knowledge of the way nature really is. The problem of creating something which is new, but which is consistent with everything which has been seen before, is one of extreme difficulty.

While I'm on this subject I want to talk about whether it will ever be possible to imagine *beauty* that we can't *see.* It is an interesting question. When we look at a rainbow, it looks beautiful to us. Everybody says, "Ooh, a rainbow." (You see how scientific I am. I am afraid to say something is beautiful unless I have an experimental way of defining it.) But how would we describe a rainbow if we were blind? We *are* blind when we measure the infrared reflection coefficient of sodium chloride, or when we talk about the frequency of the waves that are coming from some galaxy that we can't see — we make a diagram, we make a plot. For instance, for the rainbow, such a plot would be the intensity of radiation vs. wavelength measured with a spectrophotometer for each direction in the sky. Generally, such measurements would give a curve that was rather flat. Then some day, someone would discover that for certain conditions of the weather, and at certain angles in the sky, the spectrum of intensity as a function of wavelength would behave strangely; it would have a bump. As the angle of the instrument was varied only a little bit, the maximum of the bump would move from one wavelength to another. Then one day the physical review of the blind men might publish a technical article with the title "The Intensity of Radiation as a Function of Angle under Certain Conditions of the Weather." In this article there might appear a graph such as the one [shown below]. The author would perhaps remark that at the larger angles there was more radiation at long wavelengths, whereas for the smaller angles the maximum in the radiation came at shorter wavelengths. (From our point of view, we would say that the light at 40° is predominantly green and the light at 42° is predominantly red.)

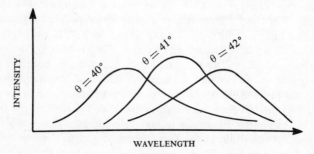

Figure 1. The intensity of electromagnetic waves as a function of wavelength for three angles (measured from the direction opposite the sun), observed only with certain meteorological conditions.

Now do we find the [accompanying] graph beautiful? It contains much more detail than we apprehend when we look at a rainbow, because our eyes cannot see the exact details in the shape of a spectrum. The eye, however, finds the rainbow beautiful. Do we have enough imagination to see in the spectral curves the same beauty we see when we look directly at the rainbow? I don't know.

But suppose I have a graph of the reflection coefficient of a sodium chloride crystal as a function of wavelength in the infrared, and also as a function of angle. I would have a representation of how it would look to my eyes if they could see in the infrared — perhaps some glowing, shiny "green," mixed with reflections from the surface in a "metallic red." That would be a beautiful thing, but I don't know whether I can ever look at a graph of the reflection coefficient of NaCl measured with some instrument and say that it has the same beauty.

On the other hand, even if we cannot see beauty in particular measured results, we *can* already claim to see a certain beauty in the equations which describe general physical laws. For example, in [a visual representation of one kind of] wave equation, there's something nice about the regularity of the appearance of the x, the y, the z, and the t. And this nice symmetry in appearance of the x, y, z, and t suggests to the mind still a greater beauty which has to do with the four dimensions, the possibility that space has four-dimensional symmetry, the possibility of analyzing that and the developments of the special theory of relativity. So there is plenty of intellectual beauty associated with the equations.

BENJAMIN LEE WHORF

Science and Linguistics

Cf. Modern English Handbook p. 1, first paragraph

Benjamin Whorf is known for his extensive work as a linguist, especially with Indian languages, although his professional work was in insurance rather than linguistics. He was a student of the pioneering linguist Edward Sapir, whose ideas are partially reflected in this material.

Every normal person in the world, past infancy in years, can and does talk. By virtue of that fact, every person — civilized or uncivilized — carries through life certain naïve but deeply rooted ideas about talking and its relation to thinking. Because of their firm connection with speech habits that have become unconscious and automatic, these notions tend to be rather intolerant of opposition. They are by no means entirely personal and haphazard; their basis is definitely systematic, so that we are justified in calling them a system of natural logic — a term that seems to me preferable to the term common sense, often used for the same thing.

According to natural logic, the fact that every person has talked fluently since infancy makes every man his own authority on the process by which he formulates and communicates. He has merely to consult a common substratum of logic or reason which he and everyone else are supposed to possess. Natural logic says that talking is merely an incidental process concerned strictly with communication, not with formulation of ideas. Talking, or the use of language, is supposed only to "express" what is essentially already formulated nonlinguistically. Formulation is an independent process, called thought or thinking, and is supposed to be largely indifferent to the nature of particular languages. Languages have grammars, which are assumed to be merely norms of conventional and social correctness, but the use of language is supposed to be guided not so much by them as by correct, rational, or intelligent THINKING.

Thought, in this view, does not depend on grammar but on laws of logic or reason which are supposed to be the same for all observers of the universe — to represent a rationale in the universe that can be "found" independently by all intelligent observers, whether they speak Chinese or Choctaw. In our own culture, the formulations of mathematics and of formal logic have acquired the reputation of dealing with this order of things: i.e., with the realm and laws of pure thought. Natural logic holds that different languages are essentially parallel methods for expressing this one-and-the-same rationale of thought and, hence, differ really in but minor ways which may seem important only because they are seen at close range. It holds that mathematics, symbolic logic, philosophy, and so on are systems contrasted with language which deal directly with this realm of thought, not that they are themselves specialized extensions of language. The attitude of natural logic is well shown in an old quip about a German grammarian who devoted his whole life to the study of the dative case. From the point of view of natural logic, the dative case and grammar in general are an extremely minor issue. A different attitude is said to have been held by the ancient Arabians: Two princes, so the story goes, quarreled over the honor of putting on the shoes of the most learned grammarian of the realm; whereupon their father, the caliph, is said to have remarked that it was the glory of his kingdom that great grammarians were honored even above kings.

The familiar saying that the exception proves the rule contains a good deal of wisdom, though from the standpoint of formal logic it became an absurdity as soon as "prove" no longer meant "put on trial." The old saw began to be profound psychology from the time it ceased to have standing in logic. What it might well suggest to us today is that, if a rule has absolutely no exceptions, it is not recognized as a rule or as anything else; it is then part of the background of experience of which we tend to remain unconscious. Never having experienced anything in contrast to it, we cannot isolate it and formulate it as a rule until we so enlarge our experience and expand our base of reference that we encounter an interruption of its regularity. The situation is somewhat analogous to that of not missing the water till the well runs dry, or not realizing that we need air till we are choking.

For instance, if a race of people had the physiological defect of being able to see only the color blue, they would hardly be able to formulate the rule that they saw only blue. The term blue would convey no meaning to them, their language would lack color terms, and their words denoting their various sensations of blue would answer to, and translate, our words "light, dark, white, black," and so on, not our word "blue." In order to formulate the rule or norm of seeing only blue, they would need exceptional moments in which they saw other colors. The phenomenon of gravitation forms a rule without exceptions; needless to say, the untutored person is utterly unaware of any law of gravitation, for it would never enter his head to conceive of a universe in which bodies behaved otherwise than they do at the earth's surface. Like the color blue with our hypothetical race, the law of gravitation is a part of the untutored individual's background, not something he isolates from that background. The law could not be formulated until bodies that always fell were seen in terms of a wider astronomical world in which bodies moved in orbits or went this way and that.

Similarly, whenever we turn our heads, the image of the scene passes across our retinas exactly as it would if the scene turned around us. But this effect is background, and we do not recognize it; we do not see a room turn around us but are conscious only of having turned our heads in a stationary room. If we observe critically while turning the head or eyes quickly, we shall see, no motion it is true, yet a blurring of the scene between two clear views. Normally we are quite unconscious of this continual blurring but seem to be looking about in an unblurred world. Whenever we walk past a tree or house, its image on the retina changes just as if the tree or house were turning on an axis; yet we do not see trees or houses turn as we travel about at ordinary speeds. Sometimes ill-fitting glasses will reveal queer movements in the scene as we look about, but normally we do not see the relative motion of the environment when we move; our psychic makeup is somehow adjusted to disregard whole realms of phenomena that are so all-pervasive as to be irrelevant to our daily lives and needs.

X Natural logic contains two fallacies: First, it does not see that the phenomena of a language are to its own speakers largely of a background character and so are outside the critical consciousness and control of the speaker who is expounding natural logic. Hence, when anyone, as a natural logician, is talking about reason, logic, and the laws of correct thinking, he is apt to be simply marching in step with purely grammatical facts that have somewhat of a background character in his own language or family of languages but are by no means universal in all languages and in no sense a common substratum of reason. Second, natural logic confuses agreement about subject matter, attained through use of language, with knowledge of the linguistic process by which agreement is attained: i.e., with the province of the despised (and to its notion superfluous) grammarian. Two fluent speakers, of English let us say, quickly reach a point of assent about the subject matter of their speech; they agree about what their language refers to. One of them, *A,* can give directions that will be carried out by the other, *B,* to *A*'s complete satisfaction. Because they thus understand each other so perfectly, *A* and *B,* as natural logicians, suppose they must of course know how it is all done. They think, e.g., that it is simply a matter of choosing words to express thoughts. If you ask *A* to explain how he got *B*'s agreement so readily, he will simply repeat to you, with more or less elaboration or abbreviation, what he said to *B*. He has no notion of the process involved. The amazingly complex system of linguistic patterns and classifications, which *A* and *B* must have in common before they can adjust to each other at all, is all background to *A* and *B*.

These background phenomena are the province of the grammarian — or of the linguist, to give him his more modern name as a scientist. The word linguist in common, and especially newspaper, parlance means something entirely different, namely, a person who can quickly attain agreement about subject matter with different people speaking a number of different languages. Such a person is better termed a polyglot or a multilingual. Scientific linguists have long understood that ability to speak a language fluently does not necessarily confer a linguistic knowledge of it, i.e., understanding of its background phenomena and its systematic processes and structure, any more than ability to play a good game of billiards confers or requires any knowledge of the laws of mechanics that operate upon the billiard table.

The situation here is not unlike that in any other field of science. All real scientists have their eyes primarily on background phenomena that cut very little ice, as such, in our daily lives; and yet their studies have a way of bringing out a close relation between these unsuspected realms of fact and such decidedly foreground activities as transporting goods, preparing food, treating the sick, or growing potatoes, which in time may become very much modified, simply because of pure scientific investigation in no way concerned with these brute matters themselves. Linguistics presents a quite similar case; the background phenomena with which it deals are involved in all our foreground activities of talking and of reaching agreement, in all reasoning and arguing of cases, in all law, arbitration, conciliation, contracts, treaties, public opinion, weighing of scientific theories, formulation of scientific results. Whenever agreement or assent is arrived at in human affairs, and whether or not mathematics or other specialized symbolisms are made part of the procedure, THIS AGREEMENT IS REACHED BY LINGUISTIC PROCESSES, OR ELSE IT IS NOT REACHED.

As we have seen, an overt knowledge of the linguistic processes by which agreement is attained is not necessary to reaching some sort of agreement, but it is certainly no bar thereto; the more complicated and difficult the matter, the more such knowledge is a distinct aid, till the point may be reached — I suspect the modern world has about arrived at it — when the knowledge becomes not only an aid but a necessity. The situation may be likened to that of navigation. Every boat that sails is in the lap of planetary forces; yet a boy can pilot his small craft around a harbor without benefit of geography, astronomy, mathematics, or international politics. To the captain of an ocean liner, however, some knowledge of all these subjects is essential.

When linguists became able to examine critically and scientifically a large number of languages of widely different patterns, their base of reference was expanded; they experienced an interruption of phenomena hitherto held universal, and a whole new order of significances came into their ken. It was found that the background linguistic system (in other words, the grammar) of each language is not merely a reproducing instrument for voicing ideas but rather is itself the shaper of ideas, the program and guide for the individual's mental activity, for his analysis of impressions, for his synthesis of his mental stock in trade. Formulation of ideas is not an independent process, strictly rational in the old sense, but is part of a particular grammar, and differs, from slightly to greatly, between different grammars. We dissect nature along lines laid down by our native languages. The categories and types that we isolate from the world of phenomena we do not find there because they stare every observer in the face; on the contrary, the world is presented in a kaleidoscopic flux of impressions which has to be organized by our minds — and this means largely by the linguistic systems in our minds. We cut nature up, organize it into concepts, and ascribe significances as we do, largely because we are parties to an agreement to organize it in this way — an agreement that holds throughout our speech community and is codified in the patterns of our language. The agreement is, of course, an implicit and unstated one, BUT ITS TERMS ARE ABSOLUTELY OBLIGATORY; we cannot talk at all except by subscribing to the organization and classification of data which the agreement decrees.

This fact is very significant for modern science, for it means that no individual is free to describe nature with absolute impartiality but is constrained to certain modes of interpretation even while he thinks himself most free. The person most nearly free in such respects would be a linguist familiar with very many widely different linguistic systems. As yet no linguist is in any such position. We are thus introduced to a new principle of relativity, which holds that all observers are not led by the same physical evidence to the same picture of the universe, unless their linguistic backgrounds are similar, or can in some way be calibrated.

This rather startling conclusion is not so apparent if we compare only our modern European languages, with perhaps Latin and Greek thrown in for good measure. Among these tongues there is a unanimity of major patterns which at first seems to bear out natural logic. But this unanimity exists only because these tongues are all Indo-European dialects cut to the same basic plan, being historically transmitted from what was long ago one speech community; because the modern dialects have long shared in

building up a common culture; and because much of this culture, on the
more intellectual side, is derived from the linguistic backgrounds of Latin
and Greek. Thus this group of languages satisfies the special case of the
clause beginning "unless" in the statement of the linguistic relativity principle at the end of the preceding paragraph. From this condition follows
the unanimity of description of the world in the community of modern
scientists. But it must be emphasized that "all modern Indo-European-
speaking observers" is not the same thing as "all observers." That modern
Chinese or Turkish scientists describe the world in the same terms as
Western scientists means, of course, only that they have taken over bodily
the entire Western system of rationalizations, not that they have corrobo-
rated that system from their native posts of observation.

When Semitic, Chinese, Tibetan, or African languages are contrasted
with our own, the divergence in analysis of the world becomes more
apparent; and, when we bring in the native languages of the Americas,
where speech communities for many millenniums have gone their ways
independently of each other and of the Old World, the fact that languages
dissect nature in many different ways becomes patent. The relativity of all
conceptual systems, ours included, and their dependence upon language
stand revealed. That American Indians speaking only their native tongues
are never called upon to act as scientific observers is in no wise to the
point. To exclude the evidence which their languages offer as to what the
human mind can do is like expecting botanists to study nothing but food
plants and hothouse roses and then tell us what the plant world is like!

Let us consider a few examples. In English we divide most of our
words into two classes, which have different grammatical and logical
properties. Class 1 we call nouns, e.g., "house, man"; class 2, verbs, e.g.,
"hit, run." Many words of one class can act secondarily as of the other
class, e.g., "a hit, a run," or "to man (the boat)," but, on the primary
level, the division between the classes is absolute. Our language thus gives
us a bipolar division of nature. But nature herself is not thus polarized. If
it be said that "strike, turn, run," are verbs because they denote temporary or short-lasting events, i.e., actions, why then is "fist" a noun? It also
is a temporary event. Why are "lightning, spark, wave, eddy, pulsation,
flame, storm, phase, cycle, spasm, noise, emotion" nouns? They are temporary events. If "man" and "house" are nouns because they are long-
lasting and stable events, i.e., things, what then are "keep, adhere, extend,
project, continue, persist, grow, dwell," and so on doing among the verbs?
If it be objected that "possess, adhere" are verbs because they are stable
relationships rather than stable percepts, why then should "equilibrium,
pressure, current, peace, group, nation, society, tribe, sister," or any kin-
ship term be among the nouns? It will be found that an "event" to us
means "what our language classes as a verb" or something analogized

therefrom. And it will be found that it is not possible to define "event, thing, object, relationship," and so on, from nature, but that to define them always involves a circuitous return to the grammatical categories of the definer's language.

In the Hopi language, "lightning, wave, flame, meteor, puff of smoke, pulsation" are verbs — events of necessarily brief duration cannot be anything but verbs. "Cloud" and "storm" are at about the lower limit or duration for nouns. Hopi, you see, actually has a classification of events (or linguistic isolates) by duration type, something strange to our modes of thought. On the other hand, in Nootka, a language of Vancouver Island, all words seem to us to be verbs, but really there are no classes 1 and 2; we have, as it were, a monistic view of nature that gives us only one class of word for all kinds of events. "A house occurs" or "it houses" is the way of saying "house," exactly like "a flame occurs" or "it burns." These terms seem to us like verbs because they are inflected for durational and temporal nuances, so that the suffixes of the word for house event make it mean long-lasting house, temporary house, future house, house that used to be, what started out to be a house, and so on.

Hopi has one noun that covers every thing or being that flies, with the exception of birds, which class is denoted by another noun. The former noun may be said to denote the class ($FC-B$) — flying class minus bird. The Hopi actually call insect, airplane, and aviator all by the same word, and feel no difficulty about it. The situation, of course, decides any possible confusion among very disparate members of a broad linguistic class, such as this class ($FC-B$). This class seems to us too large and inclusive, but so would our class "snow" to an Eskimo. We have the same word for falling snow, snow on the ground, snow packed hard like ice, slushy snow, wind-driven flying snow — whatever the situation may be. To an Eskimo, this all-inclusive word would be almost unthinkable; he would say that falling snow, slushy snow, and so on, are sensuously and operationally different, different things to contend with; he uses different words for them and for other kinds of snow. The Aztecs go even farther than we in the opposite direction, with "cold," "ice," and "snow" all represented by the same basic word with different terminations; "ice" is the noun form; "cold," the adjectival form; and for "snow," "ice mist."

What surprises most is to find that various grand generalizations of the Western world, such as time, velocity, and matter, are not essential to the construction of a consistent picture of the universe. The psychic experiences that we class under these headings are, of course, not destroyed; rather, categories derived from other kinds of experiences take over the rulership of the cosmology and seem to function just as well. Hopi may be called a timeless language. It recognizes psychological time, which is much like Bergson's "duration," but this "time" is quite unlike the mathematical time, *T,* used by our physicists. Among the peculiar properties of Hopi time are that it varies with each observer, does not permit of simultaneity, and has zero dimensions; i.e., it cannot be given a number greater than one. The Hopi do not say, "I stayed five days," but "I left on the fifth day." A word referring to this kind of time, like the word day, can have no plural. The puzzle picture [shown here] will give mental exercise to anyone who would like to figure out how the Hopi verb gets along without tenses. Actually, the only practical use of our tenses, in one-verb sentences, is to distinguish among five typical situations, which are symbolized in the picture. The timeless Hopi verb does not distinguish between the present, past, and future of the event itself but must always indicate what type of validity the SPEAKER intends the statement to have: (a) report of an event (situations 1, 2, 3 in the picture); (b) expectation of an event (situation 4); (c) generalization or law about events (situation 5). Situation 1, where the speaker and listener are in contact with the same objective field, is divided by our language into the two conditions, 1*a* and 1*b*, which it calls present and past, respectively. This division is unnecessary for a language which assures one that the statement is a report.

Hopi grammar, by means of its forms called aspects and modes, also makes it easy to distinguish among momentary, continued, and repeated occurrences, and to indicate the actual sequence of reported events. Thus the universe can be described without recourse to a concept of dimensional time. How would a physics constructed along these lines work, with no *T* (time) in its equations? Perfectly, as far as I can see, though of course it would require different ideology and perhaps different mathematics. Of course *V* (velocity) would have to go too. The Hopi language has no word really equivalent to our "speed" or "rapid." What translates these terms is usually a word meaning intense or very, accompanying any verb of motion. Here is a clue to the nature of our new physics. We may have to introduce a new term *I,* intensity. Every thing and event will have an *I,* whether we regard the thing or event as moving or as just enduring or being. Perhaps the *I* of an electric charge will turn out to be its voltage, or potential. We shall use clocks to measure some intensities, or, rather, some RELATIVE intensities, for the absolute intensity of anything will be meaningless. Our old friend acceleration will still be there but doubtless under a new name. We shall perhaps call it *V,* meaning not velocity but variation. Perhaps all growths and accumulations will be regarded as *V*'s. We should not have the concept of rate in the temporal sense, since, like velocity, rate introduces a mathematical and linguistic time. Of course we know that all measurements are ratios, but the measurements of intensities made by comparison with the standard intensity of a clock or a planet we

OBJECTIVE FIELD	SPEAKER (*Sender*)	HEARER (*Receiver*)	HANDLING OF TOPIC: A THIRD PERSON RUNNING
SITUATION 1a			ENGLISH: *He is running* HOPI: *Wari* (*Running, statement of fact*)
SITUATION 1b (*Blank*) (*devoid of running*)			ENGLISH: *He ran* HOPI: *Wari* (*Running, statement of fact*)
SITUATION 2			ENGLISH: *He is running* HOPI: *Wari* (*Running, statement of fact*)
SITUATION 3 (*Blank*)			ENGLISH: *He ran* HOPI: *Era wari* (*Running, statement of fact from memory*)
SITUATION 4 (*Blank*)			ENGLISH: *He will run* HOPI: *Warikni* (*Running, statement of expectation*)
SITUATION 5 (*Blank*)			ENGLISH: *He runs* (e.g. on the track team) HOPI: *Warikngwe* (*Running, statement of law*)

Figure 1. Contrast between a "temporal" language (English) and a "timeless" language (Hopi). What are to English differences of time are to Hopi differences in the kind of validity.

do not treat as ratios, any more than we so treat a distance made by comparison with a yardstick.

A scientist from another culture that used time and velocity would have great difficulty in getting us to understand these concepts. We should talk about the intensity of a chemical reaction; he would speak of its velocity or its rate, which words we should at first think were simply words for intensity in his language. Likewise, he at first would think that intensity was simply our own word for velocity. At first we should agree, later we should begin to disagree, and it might dawn upon both sides that different systems of rationalization were being used. He would find it very hard to make us understand what he really meant by velocity of a chemical reaction. We should have no words that would fit. He would try to explain it by likening it to a running horse, to the difference between a good horse and a lazy horse. We should try to show him, with a superior laugh, that his analogy also was a matter of different intensities, aside from which there was little similarity between a horse and a chemical reaction in a beaker. We should point out that a running horse is moving relative to the ground, whereas the material in the beaker is at rest.

One significant contribution to science from the linguistic point of view may be the greater development of our sense of perspective. We shall no longer be able to see a few recent dialects of the Indo-European family, and the rationalizing techniques elaborated from their patterns, as the apex of the evolution of the human mind, nor their present wide spread as due to any survival from fitness or to anything but a few events of history — events that could be called fortunate only from the parochial point of view of the favored parties. They, and our own thought processes with them, can no longer be envisioned as spanning the gamut of reason and knowledge but only as one constellation in a galactic expanse. A fair realization of the incredible degree of diversity of linguistic system that ranges over the globe leaves one with an inescapable feeling that the human spirit is inconceivably old; that the few thousand years of history covered by our written records are no more than the thickness of a pencil mark on the scale that measures our past experience on this planet; that the events of these recent millenniums spell nothing in any evolutionary wise, that the race has taken no sudden spurt, achieved no commanding synthesis during recent millenniums, but has only played a little with a few of the linguistic formulations and views of nature bequeathed from an inexpressibly longer past. Yet neither this feeling nor the sense of precarious dependence of all we know upon linguistic tools which themselves are largely unknown need be discouraging to science but should, rather, foster that humility which accompanies the true scientific spirit, and thus forbid that arrogance of the mind which hinders real scientific curiosity and detachment.

PERCY W. BRIDGMAN

Words, Meanings, and Verbal Analysis

Percy Bridgman was a Harvard physicist who pioneered the physics of the behavior of material under very high pressures, receiving a Nobel Prize for his experimental work in this area. His lifelong interest in philosophy of science dates from his investigations of the relativistic revolution at the beginning of the century.

Speech is almost universally employed by human beings and without it activity on the level we regard as human would be all but impossible. By means of it we communicate with each other, thus making society possible in its present form. As individuals, a large part of our mental activity consists of imagined speech with ourselves.

Nearly all the utterances of speech can be broken down, roughly and approximately, into smaller units; it may be in the first instance into sentences, and then sentences into words, and words into phonemes. For many purposes, in the languages which have been most studied, including our own, the breakdown into words is the most significant, the words being the major carrier of the meaning which we wish to communicate. We begin our examination of the nature and limitations of our intellectual tools by considering some of the things involved in the use of words.

There has been a great deal of discussion about how essential the use of words is in thinking. There are some who maintain that their own conscious thinking contains no recognizable nonverbal element, and some even go so far as to maintain that it is intrinsically impossible for thinking to be done without words. But there are, on the other hand, many others who assert with equal emphasis that a large part of their rational thinking contains no recognizable verbal element. I believe it has now come to be accepted that there is enormous variation from individual to individual in this respect. The subject has been discussed at considerable length in Hadamard's little book on the mental processes of mathematicians, where examples are given of all degrees of variation from completely verbal to almost completely nonverbal. For myself, my use of words in thinking depends to a large extent on the subject matter. When I am thinking out the design of a new piece of apparatus or driving a car through traffic my thinking contains no recognizable verbal element.

Whether or not words are an indispensable mental tool, we all are able to use them, and we do use them almost of necessity when we want to communicate with each other. In particular, this book will be written with words. Words have a definiteness and a publicity which fits them to be the subject of a first analysis. In fact, irrespective of the role played by nonverbal thinking in the intellectual processes of different people, most of the important questions with regard to the limitations of our intellectual tools can be made to present themselves in an analysis of our use of words. If we can adequately analyze what happens when we communicate with words, we shall have a very important part of the story, and probably all that we shall need for present purposes.

What, now, is this thing we call a word? Perhaps we shall ultimately be able to formulate some generalizations, but as always we shall have to begin with the concrete. One of the most obvious characteristics of any concrete individual word is that it is able to appear in the most various guises. If it is written, it may be in type or script of any style, in any color, in any size, in shorthand or longhand. If it is spoken, it may be uttered with any audible intensity, fast or slow, at any pitch, and, in most languages, with many intonations. All these so various manifestations may be of the "same" word. In what, now, does this sameness consist? Answers are possible on various levels and of various degrees of sharpness or completeness. For example, the written word which appears in print of various styles may be said to be the same if it is spelled with the same letters in the same order. But we would then have to answer what constitutes sameness in the letters, to say nothing of the fact that sometimes there are different spellings for the same word. Moreover, the philogist understands "sameness" in a word in a very broad sense and talks of the same word in different languages, or traces the history of the same word within a language, following the shifting meaning of the word during the process of linguistic evolution. It would appear, therefore, that the concept of the sameness or identity of a word is a rather loose concept, with recognizably different aspects. The particular aspect which concerns us in any concrete situation may often have to be judged by the context. This, however, is something which we do easily enough in the ordinary situations of daily life.

Our general point of view suggests that whatever it is that gives sameness or identity to a word must in some way be connected with the activities with which it is associated, either as word emitted or as word received. Now the activities associated with the particular word may be exceedingly complex and may vary widely from individual to individual. All sorts of detailed memories regarding past associations may be recognizably called to mind by the word. These may depend to a large extent on the specific experiences of the individual. More than this, a subconscious fringe of "know-how" with regard to usage of the word envelops the word. This know-how has close social involvements. It reminds one of the fringe of knowledge that surrounds our spatial perception of objects, which, among other things, enables us to anticipate and predict our motor experiences when we change our visual relation to the object. By analogy, one may speak suggestively of "verbal perception" in the same way that one speaks of space perception. Unlike our perceptions of space, an extensive social experience would appear to be necessary for the formation of verbal perceptions, but this is only a reflection of the fact that words occur predominantly in a social setting. The full background implied in verbal perception is not articulately present in consciousness, but often may be partially elicited by suitable verbal experiments. One may ask oneself "Would I use this or that word in this or that situation?" and one often finds that the answer comes with astonishing assurance.

The verbal experiment often reveals the presence of verbal compulsion — I feel that I could say nothing else in the situation. I would call verbal compulsion a special case of verbal perception. Verbal compulsion would sometimes appear to reveal the presence of unsuspected tautology. The following is an example. If at the end of an interval of time there is more of something inside a closed surface than there was at the beginning, then I, and I think other people also, feel a compulsion to say that the excess either got in across the surface or was created within the surface during the interval. The concealed tautology here would seem to be associated with the notion of creation. In the absence of an independent definition of creation, and we have not given such a definition, I am not "saying anything" when I say that the excess either crossed the surface or was created inside, but am merely saying in another way what I mean by "create." Another example is afforded by the compulsion which most people feel to say "A statement is either true or it is not true." The compulsion here may arise either because we are dealing with a concealed definition of "not," or perhaps more generally with a tautological tie-in between "statement," "true," and "not." In cases like these we may use the presence of verbal compulsion as a tool for smoking out the presence of concealed tautology.

Most people feel a compulsion in the sort of situation presented by the former traditional point of view toward axioms. These were considered as "self-evident" truths. Here "self-evident" contains an implication of compulsion. It would be interesting to analyze to what extent the compulsion felt here is a verbal compulsion reflecting the presence of concealed tautology. It is not natural to think that the compulsion formerly felt by most people in the presence of the parallel axiom of Euclid arose entirely from a concealed tautology. On the other hand, it is to be remembered that Poincaré viewed the truth of Euclidian geometry as a "convention," and such convention is pretty close to tautology.

The background of verbal perception disclosed by adroit questioning may be of unsuspected complexity and richness. In fact, the complexity and richness are so great that it would be prohibitive to attempt to describe them fully. Furthermore, the total intellectual activity associated with a given word would not be the same for any two individuals: the verbal perceptions of a poet are quite different from those of an engineer. For that matter, verbal perception need not be twice the same for the same individual. What it is that constitutes "sameness" in a word must therefore involve some very restricted aspect of the total activities associated with it.

What we are usually concerned with in words is their function in a social setting as a means of communication, and this is closely connected with the "meaning" of the word. Whatever it is that gives successive uses of a word sameness would seem to be tied up in some way with this question of meaning, except perhaps for the historian or philologist. In fact, for many purposes the meaning of a word is its most important attribute, with all due deference to poets of the school of Gertrude Stein. Now this business of the meaning of a word is not simple — books have been written on the meaning of meaning. "Meaning" may be used in a broad or a narrow sense. I have heard a noted linguist define the meaning of a word as that which is common to all its usages. This gives a first impression of great generality, but when one examines it, it appears on the contrary so narrow as to contain the possibility that it may be self-defeating. For, after the impossible requirement has been met that all the usages have been examined, the possibility remains that no common element may be discernible in all its usages. If one wants this kind of great generality, it would seem to be better to say that the meaning of a word is specified by enumerating all the conditions under which the word would be used. But this would seem to be so broad as to be self-defeating. What we want is something nearer to a minimum than a maximum specification.

The meaning of a word would seem to be located somewhere in the area of verbal perception. Just how much of verbal perception is concerned with meaning appears to be somewhat vague. Many people appear to be satisfied with their command of the meaning of a word if they have a vague feeling that they could, if they tried, tell whether they would use the word in this or that situation, without ever putting the vague feeling to the test of actual trial or usage. This may be satisfactory enough for an individual who does not care to check the success of his communications, but in a social setting it inevitably leads to confusion because the full verbal perception surrounding a word is usually different for different individuals. However, what we shall understand by meaning is associated in some way with successful communication. Furthermore, communication need not necessarily be social — I can talk to myself or I can leave a note to myself on the table to call up the grocer in the morning.

What now is the criterion for judging that an attempt at communication has been successful? It is sometimes a matter of extreme difficulty to know when communication has been successful, but it is, on the other hand, usually comparatively easy to tell when it has been unsuccessful. If the taxi driver takes you to Washington Street, instead of to Jefferson Street, for which you asked, or if you see the stranger who asked you the way taking the first right instead of the first left as you told him, you know that your attempt at communication has been unsuccessful. A general method for checking the success of a communication is to observe whether the recipient of the communication acts in the way you wanted to bring about. In the simplest situations this criterion for successful communication is fairly simple and straightforward, but, as the situation gets more complex, it becomes increasingly difficult to be sure that we have communicated what we wanted, for the communication has not been successful unless *all* the consequences that we intended are achieved. In complex situations it is difficult to check them all. Often the best we can do, when none of the obvious criteria for unsuccessful communication are satisfied, is to close our eyes and hope that we have been successful.

It is often said that all definition or communication of meaning must in the last analysis be ostensive. This, it seems to me, is a gross oversimplification. There is the story of the African explorer who tried to get the native word for table by pointing to one, and who received as many different words as there were natives in his retinue, ranging from "hard" to "round" to "black" to "four-legged," etc. Any ostensive definition can be checked only by usage in many situations, differing in all except the one feature in common which one is trying to isolate.

The consequences that we wish to achieve by our communication are almost inevitably activities of one sort or another — either overt action or mental activity which may or may not result in overt activity. The nature of the connection between the spoken or written word and the activity induced is most complex. In any event, communication between people is obviously something different in kind from the transfer of a physical object from one person to another. The word with which we communicate is not like a physical object. We, in our sophistication, can see this, but there are primitive peoples to whom a word may be a self-existent thing, with an individuality of its own which is often exploited in the practice of word magic.

The activity induced by the word has no immediate or obvious connection with the physical attributes of the word. These attributes could, for example, be given in terms of the coordinates of the groove on the phonograph record which reproduces the word when suitably coupled to a loud-speaker. The factors which determine the connection between the physical attributes of the word and the induced activity involve society and past history, as appears from the consideration that the use of words has to be learned. Speaking roughly, the locus of the most important part of whatever it is that gives a word identity and meaning is in the brains of the people that use the word. Given only the physical word, that is, the sound of the spoken word or the appearance of the written word, neither the activity associated with it or its meaning may be discovered. The association between the physical word and the meaning is almost always arbitrary, and if the continuity of the thread of association in the minds of the people who use the word is broken, the meaning may not be recovered. It is only because the thread of continuity in human brains has not been completely severed that we have been able, by enormous effort, to read the writings of the Mayas or the ancient Cretans.

Whatever the meaning of a word may be, it would seem therefore to be something which does not pertain to the word as such, but to the whole complex environment in which use of the word is embedded, and in particular pertains to the user of the word. From this point of view it is not the word as it stands in isolation on the printed page which means something, but I who read the word, or you who wrote the word, who means something. Emphasis on the activity aspect of the word demands that this not be lost sight of. A simple verbal trick is helpful in this connection. Never ask "What does word X mean?" but ask instead "What do I mean when I say word X?" or "What do you mean when you say word X?" To agree to talk about meaning only in this sort of setting constitutes a considerable curtailment of conventional linguistic usage, which uses such expressions, for example, as "The word X *has* such and such a meaning." An instructive exhibition of the many linguistic contexts in which the words "mean" and "meaning" occur is afforded by a paper by Jason Xenakis in *Methodos* 6 (1954), 299–329. But, although we may renounce the possibility of saying many of the things which Xenakis says, I do not believe that we are making any essential surrender if we agree to talk about meaning in this book in such a way that it is only you and I that mean something when we say something, the physical utterance having no meaning as such. I do not have to convince you that it is good tactics to accept this limitation of the usage of "meaning." All that is required is that you admit that it is a legitimate question to ask "What do I mean when I say thus and so?" and that you will be willing to make a serious attempt to answer it. This I think is not asking or expecting too much. In spite of our agreement we may often find it convenient, because it is shorter, to use "meaning" in the common way as something that words *have*. But when I ask whether I understand the meaning of a word

I shall understand that this is a paraphrase for "What do I (or you) mean when I (or you) use the word?"

I suppose that my command of the meaning of a word could be called complete if I could exhaustively enumerate the conditions which would lead me to use the word myself and could infer from the usage of the word by you in any particular situation what were the conditions which had dictated use of the word by you. This is what I shall understand by meaning in the most general sense. That is, I shall say that I know the meaning of a word if I can state the conditions which dictate use of the word by you or by me. It would seem that this covers most of what we are usually interested in. It is, of course, only very seldom that we attempt as articulate an analysis [as] this of our meanings. We are usually satisfied with a vague feeling that we could state the conditions if we wanted to, without ever taking the trouble actually to do it.

I suspect that we are more likely to demand that our neighbor make an analysis for meaning of the words that he uses than to make it for ourselves. When we do get around to attempting such an analysis, I think we discover that we have certain ideals for our meanings; we are not satisfied with a mere factual description of the conditions under which we do actually use our words, but we want our usage to satisfy certain restrictions. The necessity for some sort of restriction is obvious, because we are trying to accomplish some purpose by our verbalizing, usually communication. Some of the restrictions are obvious enough. We would like our meanings to have a degree of stability in time, so that the meaning of a word tomorrow is the same as today. We are not too much disturbed by a slow change of the meaning over centuries — the meaning of many words in Elizabethan English is recognizably different from the meaning today. We would probably prefer that the meanings be unique, although we do put up with many words in English which have multiple meanings. As a special case of uniqueness we would probably prefer that the meaning not depend on the person using the word, although every parent has been able to understand the private meanings of his children while they are learning to talk, and children can talk to each other in their own private code.

There is a special class of words which is of great interest in this connection, of which perhaps the most important example is "I." The particular person indicated by "I" is different for every user. Shall we therefore say that the meaning of "I" is different for every user? Some people would probably say just this; whether we do or not is to a certain extent a matter of choice and a matter of words. I personally would prefer to say that the "referent" that is, the specific object indicated, is different for different users of "I," but that the meaning is the same, because the conditions which determine its use are the same. But there is here a certain vagueness. What shall we understand by "conditions"? Obviously it is not my intention to call the conditions the same only if the actual concrete referent is the same for different users, for this state of affairs never occurs. The sameness of conditions which I fasten on is the *relation* of the user to the referent. "I" refers to the user himself, to whom the user stands in the relation of identity. The matter is not obvious or uniquely necessary, and usage has to be learned by observation of social practice. This is something that we all manage to learn somehow in childhood; from this distance we may be inclined to wonder how we managed to be bright enough to learn it. I find it particularly hard to see how we managed to learn it if those psychologists are right who maintain that the concept of "I" is the last to form, and comes only after much experience in society of other persons. It must be very puzzling for the child to hear other people about him continually saying "I," each person referring to something different.

The meaning of "I" is "relational," and "I" is a relational word. It will be my thesis in later chapters that there are many other similar relational words — many more than are usually recognized — and that recognition of the relational character of many of these words may profoundly alter our conception of such things as the relation of individual and society.

There is an elaborate formal discipline dealing with distinctions such as between "referent" and "meaning" exemplified by the *Theory of Signs* of Charles W. Morris, in which occur such words as "semiosis," "semiotic," "semantics," and "pragmatics." We do not need these for our simple purposes, for we can conduct our analysis without such formal machinery.

Returning to the general examination of meanings, among the many ideals we have for our meanings surely one of the most important is that our meanings be as sharp as possible; absolute sharpness is, of course, unattainable. One of the most potent sources of irritation in daily life is slipshod use of ambiguous meanings. In most cases no elaborate machinery is required for the elimination of the irritating ambiguity; usually it would be sufficient merely that the speaker imagine himself in the place of the hearer and ask himself whether the hearer could reconstruct the situation given only the uttered words. In practice, of course, the hearer has other things to guide him than just the spoken words, so that it does not usually put too onerous a burden on the speaker to achieve a sufficiently unambiguous communication. If only some speakers did not demand it as a right that the hearer figure out for himself what the speaker must have had in mind.

For most purposes we can get along sufficiently well with only casual attention to sharpness, but when real differences of opinion arise, the first thing that should be done is to sharpen the meanings. Every debator knows that a preliminary to any fruitful debate is to define the terms. Ordinarily the meanings are taken so much as a matter of course that often the mere challenge to make more articulate what one means will result in considerable clarification. It is not hard to form the habit of asking oneself as a preliminary to any particular piece of analysis "What do I mean by this or that term?" with consequent disclosure of many factors usually overlooked. For scientific purposes the necessity for a high degree of sharpness is so great as to demand special consideration and the use of special techniques. In those cases where scientific statements can be put in mathematical form the presumption is good that sharpness has been attained merely because mathematics is itself precise. But this is by no means the whole story, because the quantities which enter the mathematical equations themselves have to be obtained by a procedure of some sort, and this procedure may or may not be precise. Consider, for example, Fechner's law in psychology that the intensity of a sensation is proportional to the logarithm of the intensity of the stimulus. The ostensible mathematical precision of this law is illusory until procedures are worked out for measuring with precision the intensity of a stimulus or the intensity of a sensation.

One method of attaining improved sharpness of meaning which is particularly useful for scientific terms is to subject them to an "operational" analysis. This is a subject which I have discussed in much detail in other places and about which there has been much misunderstanding. There is no point in repeating the details of this discussion here. For the present it will be sufficient to remark that an operation is an activity. Later I shall return to the matter, for there are several questions connected with operational analysis which I have long been waiting a chance to discuss. These include considerations with regard to the nature of the operations themselves, and applications of operational analysis to situations for which I have, up to the present, given no analysis.

For the present we shall assume that enough has now been said about words and their meanings to provide a basis for the attack on the problem of finding the meaning of any concrete word; this in general demands a formulation of the conditions of its use.

There is more to the question of meaning than the meaning of individual words — words are used together in combination, and it is the meaning of the whole combination which usually is of primary interest. New questions arise when we deal with combinations of words. The meaning of a combination is not simply the sum of the meanings separately; that is, the conditions which dictate the use of the words in combination is not the mere sum or the juxtaposition of the conditions which dictated the use of the words separately. There is no simple addition law for the meanings of words combined into sentences, any more than there is an addition law for the meaning of phonemes combined into words. Here we have a legitimate example of "emergence" as opposed to the many illegitimate claims for emergence in biological or social situations.

The combination of words often involves the imposition of additional restrictions by the mere form of the combination. The combination may, for example, take the form of a statement, in which case it is implied that a truth value attaches to the statement. Possibly there is the further implication that there is some method of verifying the truth of the statement. Or the combination may take the form of a question. In this case it is implied that it does not involve logical contradiction to assume that there is a procedure for finding the answer to the question and for checking the correctness of the answer. Furthermore, I think we usually feel that we have a right to demand that one may not ask a question unless he is prepared to say what kind of an answer would be satisfactory. This requirement throws out of court a great many words combined into the grammatical form of a question. For example, many questions beginning with "why" are of this sort. Such, in the context of daily life, are frequently not legitimate questions at all, but are merely invitations to speculation. I think many people ask questions with only the most nebulous sort of an idea of what a satisfactory answer might be like, hoping that when the answer is supplied to them *ex machina* they will at the same time see a little more clearly what it was that they had vaguely in the back of their heads when they asked the question. As a tool of individual enlightenment this procedure may have its justification, but it is a one-sided sort of transaction that cannot commend itself equally to both parties. The asking and the answering should be a cooperative enterprise. It must nevertheless be recognized that it may be a fruitful tool of exploration into new territory to ask oneself questions which seem sensible from their form, judging by past experience, but for which one at the moment has no answer and no idea what sort of an answer might be satisfactory. An example might be "Why does negative electricity attract positive?" The value of asking questions like this is that it affords a stimulus to try to imagine what sort of an answer might conceivably be satisfactory, and under this stimulus fresh aspects of the situation may come to light. One may set oneself to acquiring the knack of formulating scientific (or other) questions useful from this point of view. It is to be considered whether a background of scientific (or other) experience is necessary, or to what extent verbal experience alone will lead to fruitful results. One could perhaps make an argument for the expectation that verbal experience in the individual would be fruitful, since the verbal experience of the individual has as a background verbal experience of the race, and this has been closely coupled by evolutionary adaptation to the external environment. In any event, the actual asking of the question by the individual is a verbal operation, and an important kind of operation, at that. There is, however, the danger that one may remain on the verbal level and this danger has to be continually guarded against. For instance, is the question "Why am I I and not you?" anything more than a combination of words? If anyone has the urge to find something back of his impulse to ask this question it becomes a problem to find the significance of the urge. I suspect that a good deal of philosophy has had its origin in the endeavor to find verbally satisfactory answers to questions that sounded as though they ought to have answers.

Another sort of combination of words in which the meaning of the whole depends on the form of the combination as well as on the words individually is a command. "Eat your spinach" means more than could be inferred from the meanings of the three words separately.

Grammar is the name of the discipline that deals with aspects of the ways in which words may be combined if the combination is to have meaning as a whole, but grammar is not coextensive with the whole question of the meaning of combinations of words. There are grammatical combinations of words that have no meaning — "Virtue is blue" — and there are ungrammatical combinations that are meaningful — "Women is nuts." We do not need to attempt a necessary and sufficient characterization of what grammar is — roughly it would seem to be concerned with the rules governing the permissible association of certain types of words with other types. Grammatical speech can largely be learned by observation of the grammatical speech of others without the articulate formulation of the rules. It is an interesting exercise for the imagination to try to reconstruct the historical steps by which grammar developed. Which came first — individual words or combinations of words? It would seem probable that the usage of words and of combinations of words developed hand in hand, and that only after the language was an accomplished fact did some contemplative grammarian see what had happened. There are languages, such as some of the North American Indian languages, in which the analysis into individual words is much less clean cut than in the Indo-European languages, and what corresponds to a sentence is more like a single long compound word put together by the successive addition of separable prefixes and suffixes.

The question of why it is that utterances are analyzable into words is similar to the question of why words are analyzable into phonemes, a fact which made possible the invention of the alphabet. Perhaps both these questions are only invitations to speculation, but, at any rate in the case of the second question, a glimpse of what might constitute a satisfactory answer is afforded by a consideration of the physiological constitution of the biological machinery that utters the words.

The subconscious feeling of the limitations imposed by grammar on combinations of words is contained in what I have called the fringe of verbal perception that surrounds a word — it is formed only after long experience and is by no means the same in different people.

Perhaps the most sweeping of all the rules of language is that words of one language may not be combined with words of another language. This, of course, at once brings up the question of what is a "language." The answer is not sharp — there will not always be agreement about whether some local pattern of speech should be called a dialect or a language. Neither is the rule sharp that words of one language may not be combined with those of another — the rule is often consciously violated by those who would achieve a meretricious elegance in their style. But the rule may be violated for better reasons. Only in the simplest cases are words in one language completely equivalent to those in another. Usually there are recognizable differences in the perceptual fringe that surrounds a word in different languages, so that seldom is an exact translation possible from one language to another. It may be that English, for example, possesses no word of the precise shade of meaning that a particular situation demands, but that some foreign language does. In this case a meticulous writer will not hesitate to insert the foreign word in the English sentence.

It is interesting to ask about the order of events in a situation like this. Would the shade of meaning of the English word be felt unsatisfactory if one did not already have at one's command the foreign word? Or does one have some vague criterion, not formulated in language, which the word must satisfy, and then does one seek for it in any language at one's command? The deeper one probes into the mechanism by which one fits a word to a situation the more convinced one will become of the importance of unformulated and even unconscious mental processes.

Vaguenesses with respect to what a language is do not make much trouble in practice, but it is usually clear enough what we have in mind when we talk about a language in the context of our every day life. But when we want to achieve greater sharpness we have to refine the everyday notion of a language as being predominantly a speech pattern practised by people associated with a restricted geographical area. It turns out that it is profitable to make distinctions depending on the subject matter, and we talk of the "language of physics" or the "language of biology." The decision of subject matter is fairly straight forward in the case of usage like this. The matter becomes more sophisticated, however, when we try to characterize the subject matter in logical terms. We may, for example, want to understand by a language all those words which can occur in a single logically consistent system. By a logical system we may understand all those statements that can be deduced by the rules of logic from a set of fundamental postulates in conjunction with a set of terms that are accepted as unanalyzed. In the "language" of this logical system it would not have meaning to ask what is the meaning of one of the undefined terms. But with a different set of postulates and a different set of undefined terms the term in question might be analyzed and so a meaning given to it. The language of the second logical system thus enables us to ask questions about the first which the first could not ask about itself. The second language is a "metalanguage" with respect to the first. The metalanguage may in turn have a language "meta-" with respect to it, and in fact it would be possible to construct an unlimited hierarchy of successive metalanguages. Precise analysis of the construction of the first logical language and the succeeding metalanguages has been carried to a high degree of refinement by professional logicians and is most important for logical precision. An example of the sort of situation to which analysis in terms of metalanguages leads is afforded by Tarski's celebrated analysis of truth. According to this analysis the *statement* "snow is white" is verified if snow is white. The second occurrence of "white" is in the metalanguage with respect to its first occurrence. But when we have done our best and have constructed the last metalanguage necessary for our purpose we find that we are still using English words (or the words of whatever happens to be our native tongue), so that the system of metalanguages is embedded in the single language of daily life. We are still left with the problem of understanding our language of daily life and discovering what the meanings are that can be expressed in that language and what degree of sharpness we can hope to attain. For our purposes in the following we shall not bother much with metalanguages but shall address ourselves directly to what seem to me more immediate problems.

The fact that we are going to try to get along without the formal machinery of metalanguages does not mean that we can close our eyes to the basic characteristics of situations that invite the analysis into hierarchies of language. It is only that we shall try to be less formal. Furthermore, an analysis into metalanguages would have for us the disadvantage of implying the possibility of unattainable precision. In any event, we shall often find ourselves operating on one or another "level," and the different levels correspond roughly to the different metalanguages. But the levels are not sharp, and we shall find it almost impossible to avoid shifting back and forth from one level to another, even in the same sentence. This suggests that "level" may not be a very good figure for describing what actually happens, but it does have the advantage of suggestiveness.

The structure of language is not always such that it facilitates recognition of different levels, and considerable logical practise may be necessary to specify them. Facility in handling the affairs of daily life would often be hampered by stopping to recognize the logical niceties, so that for some purposes a language may be better fitted to survive if it does not offer a machinery by which these nice distinctions may be made. A simple example will illustrate. Ancient Babylonian had different words for a letter and for the character that represents the letter. Modern English ignores the difference; in fact it is hard to say in English that the letter, as such, is not the same as the character which represents it. Yet there are situations where the Babylonian distinction naturally presents itself to the user of English. For instance, we might want to say to a stone-cutter, "The 'A' which you just carved in that inscription is too small." It is easy to imagine that the desirability of making the distinction arose in Babylon precisely because of the enormous labor required to make cuneiform records on clay tablets. At any rate, here is an example of the use of a word on two levels in English, and two distinct words in another language corresponding to the two levels of English.

Often a writer or speaker may be conscious of operating on a level different from the usual one, and he may find it desirable to call explicit attention to it by using some special device. Thus, in the case of the letter A above, he might say "the letter, as a letter," or, if he is writing, he may enclose the letter in quotation marks, as we did above. This situation often occurs with respect to individual words; we may be concerned with them in their capacity as words and this may be indicated by the use of quotation marks, a device which I shall often use. A word handled in this way functions as a noun, irrespective of what part of speech it may be in ordinary usage.

The situation presented by two levels in the usage of "letter" is suggestive of a very broad class of situations. We often have occasion to talk about talking, and there are many words in English for use on just such occasions. The situations thus presented are of indefinite complexity. For not only can we talk about talking by the use of words devised for the express purpose, but then we can talk about our use of these new words, or, otherwise expressed, talk about talking about talking. The regress has no end. The regress occurs whether we look at the situation in static existential terms, as we imagine the Babylonian, did, or whether we look at it in terms of activity, as we may when we consider that talking itself is an activity which continually creates itself as we talk, so that the very act of talking itself creates new topics for conversation which did not exist before we started.

It is surprising to discover, on making the detailed analysis, how many of the puzzling questions occur in a context of talking about talking. The simple terms of logic are of this category, such as "if" and "or." Or some of the simplest terms of daily life, such as the "past" or the "future," are of this class. For what is the past more than a word which we use in talking about events that have already happened, or the future more than a word that we use in discussing plans? Even if one maintains that there *is* much more to past or future than this, nevertheless for most purposes we do not need this something more, for we can get along perfectly well without agreeing on a formulation of what more it is.

About all that one can do about talking is to talk about it. Here again we have a system dealing with itself. How shall we understand our tools if the only tools of understanding are the tools themselves? It seems doubtful to me whether such situations can ever be dealt with in a completely satisfactory way or whether we can ever lay the ghost of the infinite regress. One questions the fundamental validity of the whole enterprise of language. At best it would seem that there must be limitations of some sort here, and one of our problems is to find what they are.

Many of the puzzling issues of daily life, which we unconsciously realize we have not learned to cope with, are on the verbal level. For example, the age-old problem of the freedom of the will is on the verbal level. We *say* that we are free, but there is no objective proof that we really are. The problem of the freedom of the will is to reconcile this that we say with other things that we say, such as that everything is subject to law.

On the legal plane such concepts as human rights and justice are mostly things that we say about our relations to each other. The problem of the critically minded lawyer is to a large extent to discover how he can weld the things that we want to say about these relations into a consistent verbal edifice whose parts are logically tied to each other.

Two of the most important human enterprises are almost entirely on the verbal level. The first is philosophy. Certainly the part of philosophy which is open to observation is verbal — what is written in books or what is said by one philosopher to another. The philosopher uses no material instruments — he does not go into the laboratory or even collect statistics. His primary concern is to get our experience into as verbally satisfactory a form as possible. Most philosphers do not like to have the predominantly verbal nature of their enterprise insisted upon. They apparently feel, in my opinion unnecessarily, that this implies a pejorative attitude toward the importance of what they do. The favorite tool of the philosopher is the verbal experiment. He tries this or that form of expression and he asks, "Would you regard this way of talking about it as satisfactory?" Even if we try to go beyond the verbal level and ask what it is that the philosopher is trying to get into words, we see that the philosopher is primarily interested in a particular sort of subject matter. He is interested in an aspect of human activity, as distinguished from the unlimited activity of the whole external world that characterizes the interest of the physicist or the chemist or the biologist. This aspect of human behavior primarily is thinking, and we may, if we think it is more consistent with the dignity of the philosopher than insisting on the verbal aspect of what he does, say that the philosopher is concerned with thinking about thinking. But even so, he is interested only in certain aspects of thinking, the aspects which find their most immediate expression in verbal behavior and not in the explanatory and descriptive aspects which concern the psychologist. Of course the dividing line is not sharp, as shown by the fact that formerly psychology was treated as a subdivision of philosophy. Roughly, the primary concern of the philosopher seems to be how he shall talk about what he thinks and what he says. In doing this it seems to me that he is sometimes tempted to treat verbal activity as a self-contained activity, worth pursuing for its own sake. It seems to me that he is inclined to hope that there must be some meaning in any grammatical combination of words, particularly when they deal with abstractions, and that he regards it as one of his problems to discover what this meaning may be.

The second great human enterprise, almost exclusively verbal, is logic. Simple observation shows that this, as well as philosophy, is conducted almost exclusively on the verbal level. But logic is subject to a control that philosophy is not, the control of "truth," for logic offers a method of passing from initial statements to other statements of such a nature that if the initial statements are true the statements to which one passes are also true. This puts the enterprise of logic in a special category.

It would appear that in general a large part of the serious enterprise of the race is precisely to discover how the various things that we want to say can be welded into a verbally consistent whole. Individuals differ widely in their attitude toward this human enterprise. Many act as though they take it with a deathly seriousness and regard the successful solution of the problem as of transcendent importance. I suspect that most religious fanatics and a good many lawyers are this type of person. To others it does not seem so important that everything should be got into a verbally consistent whole, provided only that they can deal with each new situation as it arises. This attitude is fortified by a certain cynicism with regard to the possibility of carrying out so ambitious a program of getting *everything* into a verbally consistent whole, a cynicism which has a certain justification when the haphazard origin of the whole human linguistic apparatus is considered.

Eventually, of course, we have to stop talking about talking — the regress cannot actually be carried to infinity. Where we stop is almost as important as what we say before we stop. For example, the "ultimate particle" of physics probably only marks the place where the structure of experimental knowledge forces us to stop talking. Other fields of verbal activity are not so fortunate in having an exernally imposed cut-off point and, in consequence, may never make their emergence from the verbal level. In general, our verbal machinery has no mechanism for automatically shutting itself off beyond its range of applicability, a feature which, as I have emphasized in some of my earlier writings, also characterizes mathematics.

In spite of all the limitations which we can thus see in the verbal process I shall not hesitate, when it suits my purpose, to exploit the verbal nature of many of our activities. This is to a certain extent making a virtue of necessity, for it is an inexorable fact that the written page which I am now writing and which you are now reading is composed of words. I as I write and you as you read cannot get away from words, any more than I can get away from myself. This is a simple matter of observation. Any effects which I can here produce on you must be through the medium of words. It is a tautology to say that our verbal communication, which includes nearly all significant human communication, cannot get away from words. It may strike the reader as surprising that I would be willing to adopt so tolerant an attitude toward the purely verbal by admitting this necessity of operating on the verbal level, if he remembers that I have often insisted on the importance of an eventual emergence of our operations onto the nonverbal level. This necessity is still as imperative as ever, particularly for the physicist when he attempts to form concepts which will be useful to him. However, on the printed page I am compelled to express this nonverbal emergence in verbal terms. This is accomplished by the use of different types of words — the referents for some kinds of words are nonverbal activities, it may be operations in the laboratory with instruments, whereas the referents for other words are recognizably still verbal activities. The words in which the physicist defines the meaning of such concepts as "length" must be of the type that have nonverbal referents — no more can be demanded. And even here we have to get back onto the verbal level if we wish to communicate the results of our nonverbal operations. Verbal operation is thus a pretty pervasive thing, and it is important to understand what is involved as well as we can.

The advantages, on occasion, of concentrating attention on the verbal nature of communication and thought are that in many contexts we do not need anything more for our purposes and can save ourselves many of the embarrassments that arise when we imply that there is something more. In this way we can automatically keep out many of the questions that I call metaphysical. For example, in discussing such things as length or velocity or momentum, usually and perhaps always, we need only to be able to specify the conditions under which we would use the *word* length or velocity or momentum. We do not need to ask "What *is* length or velocity or momentum?" a form of question which often has unfortunate metaphysical implications. However, a nonmetaphysical meaning *can* be assigned, when the context makes it desirable, to the question "What is length," for we can say "Length is a number obtained by a special instrumental procedure" and we can specify the procedure if required. The two approaches are not inconsistent, however, for we can paraphrase the instrumental operational approach by saying "I use the word length to indicate that I have obtained a number by such and such an instrumental procedure." We are here obviously operating on different levels and it does not seem possible to keep them sharply distinct. The physicist will not be confused by all this, but will still realize that the number and the procedure are the important things for him.

Going still further, abstractions in general can be dealt with on the verbal level. Thus we can always say, when pressed to say what truth or time or existence or any other abstraction *is,* that these are words which we use under such and such conditions. Or, instead of asking "What *are* external objects?" we find that it is quite sufficient to ask "What do I mean when I say that there are external objects?" It is surprising, when one tries it, to find how many situations can be adequately dealt with in this way, and how seldom we need anything more. This is obviously true in most situations involving communication, for most communication is verbal. Whenever it turns out that this is all we need, it would appear that there "is" nothing more.

I think a great many people feel that a verbal approach to abstractions is so superficial that they will be unwilling to make it. For instance, in trying to answer the question "What *is* virtue?" they will be unwilling to answer by saying "I use the word 'virtue' in such and such circumstances" because of their feeling that so much essential is disregarded in such a statement. I think most of the prejudice to such an approach can be overcome if such people could learn to say "Whatever virtue may 'really be,' it *at least* has its verbal aspect" and learn to realize that they have not mastered their understanding of virtue until they can account for all its aspects, including the verbal. When they have learned to make this approach I think they will be surprised to find how often it meets all their needs. And I believe that everyone is capable of learning how to make this verbal approach.

There are certain types of situation which language, as conventionally used, cannot deal with without an embarrassment that comes pretty close to being the embarrassment of self-contradiction. Some of these are self-reflective situations in which we try to say that there are certain situations that language is incapable of dealing with. The embarrassment comes when we attempt to say what the situation is, which we usually feel an irresistible impulse to do. But, manifestly, it is impossible to express in language a situation which language is incapable of expressing. As an illustration we may take the example probably originally due to Kant, although it seems to have been independently discovered a number of times since, that it is impossible to distinguish in words alone between a right- and a left-handedness. This example is often hailed as one of unusual profundity, but I believe the profundity is fictitious. For language is never capable of specifying in terms only of itself the concrete referent for any word whatever, but always we have to point eventually, and the pointing itself becomes significant only in the context of indefinite repetition in a fixed cultural background.

Some people like to say that the success of language in dealing with the world around us is due to the similarity of structure of language and the world. If the structures were not similar, they say, language would not be capable of dealing with the world. The late Count Korzybski and his disciples were particularly prone to say this. To me, if there was ever a glittering generality that is repudiated by simple observation, it is this one.

There is another type of situation in which conventional language is embarrassed. These are the situations discussed, for example, by Quine in his *From a Logical Point of View* under the heading of "nonbeing." We cannot say that such a thing as a square circle, for example, does not "exist" without implying by the mere fact that we are using the words and talking about "it" that a square circle has a certain kind of existence. What kind of existence this may be has provided philosophy with a topic of discussion for thousands of years. The quandary presented by this situation we can see is one which naturally arises in the Indo-European languages — it would be interesting to know whether it is felt as a quandary in other types of language. It seems to me that the situation can be adequately dealt with by reducing it to the purely formal verbal level. If we say "The combination of words 'square circle' has no referent either in the objective external world or in the conceptual world of logically consistent objects," it seems to me that we have said all that we need to say. I do not see why philosophers are not willing to say this and dismiss the topic from serious consideration.

A somewhat similar paradoxical and embarrassing situation arises whenever we make a statement of the form "The statement A has no meaning." For if the statement A did not have a meaning of sorts, we would not be able to assent to the statement that it has no meaning. We may recognize this "meaning of sorts" as a second kind of meaning, which may be defined in terms of the response elicited when the statement is made. If the response elicited is always the same or if the different responses have recognizable elements in common, then it may be socially useful, and it may be in accord with the usual implications of language, as used, to admit a second sort of meaning. The primary meaning of meaning would then be sought in the purposes and operations leading to the usage, and the second meaning of meaning in the response actually elicited in the given cultural context by the particular verbal combination. We might be able to get along with this sort of situation, and I think popular usage as a matter of fact does, but we would have to admit such questions as: "What is the meaning of the meaningless statement A?" Although perhaps possible, it seems to me that it is too confusing to admit this second sort of meaning, and I shall endeavor to find other ways of talking. I would be willing, for example, to speak of the implications of the meaningless statement A, reserving "meaningless" for a somewhat restricted technical use which does not correspond to its full usage in everyday life. In later chapters we will encounter examples in which I think we are, as a matter of fact, concerned with this second usage for "meaning." Some of these are of the greatest social significance.

The situations with which language deals are in a continual state of flux, yet language forces us to deal with them with a vocabulary of a finite number of discrete words with approximately fixed meanings. One may anticipate infelicities and ineptnesses; the wonder is that we are able to get along as well as we do. Our use of static words is analogous to our analysis of the world around us into things — individual, discrete, constant, and static — whereas it has been obvious from at least the time of the Greeks that "all things flow." It must be that it is a necessary characteristic of human thinking machinery to operate with fixed elements which recur. It is meaningless to ask how the world would appear if we did not see it in terms of things that recur, or what our thought would be like if it were not tied to language.

The structure and the use of language are such that we seem forever condemned to get along with only a partial description of what introspection reveals is happening. Our sentences do not leap instantaneously and full grown into being, in spite of the fact that we usually treat them as static complete structures, but they are uttered in time, and we can see that things are happening during the uttering. Meanings grow in time, and this growth implies transient effects which we seem to be incapable of getting into adequate verbal expression. Popular usage is not completely unaware of this situation but recognizes that the order in time of the component words in a sentence is not a matter of indifference. Nearly everyone can see that it is better to say "Please pass the butter" than to say "Pass the butter, please." Social success may depend on the recognition of niceties of this sort. It is a problem for the future to devise an introspectional microscope to reveal the "fine structure" of the transient detail.

The language of much of daily life — the language of the family and particularly the language of women — comes much closer to being an instrument which recognizes the fluent nonrecurring nature of things than the somewhat idealized academic thing which has been the subject of our discussion. In this language of daily life words do not have a frozen meaning, but much greater flexibility is attained. Speech in daily life is often obviously only part of a process, and it may have significance only in the immediate context. Language is thus used to suggest what is going on at that moment in the mind of the utterer, and the utterer, pariculary if a woman, expects that the listener will accept the speech in the spirit intended, and try to deduce what was going on in the utterer's mind. The same word, used a second time in a later sentence, naturally does not have the same context as on the first use, so that there is no assurance that the meaning is the same on the second use as on the first. In fact, under conditions such as these, there is no reason why even the principle of contradiction need govern the successive uses of a word or successive enunciations of the same statement. Examples of the failure of the principle of contradiction have probably been observed by everyone in family life. I recently encountered a particularly glaring example in which my wife was not even embarrassed when it was called to her attention — on the contrary. Such usage of language is more of an art than the ordinary man can achieve, and when I was asking above for a method of using language better adapted to dealing with the fluent nature of experience I had hoped for a somewhat different sort of solution.

STEPHEN TOULMIN

Scientific Theories and Scientific Myths

Stephen Toulmin is a British philosopher who is interested primarily in the philosophy and history of science. The present selection is the first part of three in the original paper; the other two parts point to possible examples of scientific myths based on cosmology and evolution.

If we go into an eighteenth-century library, we may be surprised at the number of theological works it contains. Baxter's *Reasons,* Ogden's *Articles,* Warburton's *Divine Legation*: there they stand, and with them the sermons, row on row of them, solid, calf-bound, imposing; yet somehow (we feel) period pieces, as foreign to us in our days as the wigs and top-boots in a Hogarth print. For a member of Dr. Johnson's Literary Club, it was as important to be *au fait* with Ogden or Warburton

S. Toulmin, R. W. Hepburn, A. MacIntyre. *Metaphysical Beliefs.* (S.C.M. Press Ltd., London, 1957). The full essay is entitled "Contemporary Scientific Mythology." Reprinted by permission of the Student Christian Movment Press Limited.

as it was to be ready with an apt quotation from Pope or Horace. Anyone who has read his Boswell knows how often, when gossip was exhausted, conversation in Johnson's circle turned to ethics, philosophy or theology; for these were subjects in which any educated man felt an obligation to be interested.

We in the twentieth century, however, feel different obligations. It is science we like to be up-to-date in, Freud and Hoyle we choose to know about. We are interested less in the doctrine of the First Cause than in physical cosmology, while the Ten Commandments and the nature of the moral sense seem tepid to us when set alongside the theory of the super-ego. *Autres temps autres mœrs*: the emphasis in polite conversation has shifted. If we are puzzled by the shelves of collected sermons in our ancestors' libraries, that is because we forget how far scientific and aesthetic questions have replaced moral and theological ones as the staple of dinner-table-talk; and how far the popular scientist has won over the audience of the popular preacher.

At first sight, this appears a remarkable change, and certainly, so far as prestige is concerned, science has made great advances at the expense of philosophy and theology: that much is a commonplace. But is the change as great as it seems? Are people really no longer interested in all those serious topics which preoccupied their ancestors, finding themselves absorbed instead in some quite different set of problems? Or are the same old cargoes being carried (so to speak) in fresh bottoms, under a new flag? What answer we give to that question depends on this: how far the problems the man-in-the-street expects the scientist to solve for him are ones about which a scientist is specially qualified to speak. So before we are too impressed by the change it is worth asking whether, when we turn to works of popular science, the questions we are interested in are always genuinely scientific ones. I think this is only partly so, and in what follows I shall try to show why. Often enough, we tend to ask too much of science, and to read into the things the scientist tells us implications that are not there — which in the nature of the case cannot be there; drawing from scraps of information about, for instance, physics, conclusions which no amount of physics could by itself establish. Sometimes our questions are clearly the same as those that the eighteenth-century theologians tackled: a discussion about free-will is none the less about free-will for bringing in Heisenberg's 'uncertainty relation.' But more often we are unaware of what we are doing, and turn to the scientist as to an expert, an authority, even when he is entitled to no more than a private opinion.

Quite a lot of popular science books encourage us in this, and present these opinions as the latest results of scientific research. Their authors do not confine themselves to explaining some scientific investigation, some novel theory or discovery about phenomena which had previously not been understood. They go on to do something more, something different, something which can hardly be called science at all. As a result there has grown up a sort of scientific harlequinade in the shape of an independent body of ideas which play a considerable part in the layman's picture of science, but in science proper none at all. The Running-Down Universe, Evolution with a capital E: these are two examples which (I shall try to show) are not so much scientific discoveries as scientific myths.

"Scientific Myths": the very phrase is apt to sound a little paradoxical. For we like to think of myths as a thing of the past. We pride ourselves that they have been killed, and killed, furthermore, by science. Atlas, Ceres, Wotan, Poseidon . . . *nous n'avons pas besoin de ces hypothèses.* These names are for us the last relics of an outmoded system of thought, which attempted to explain in one way — by personification — things which we can now explain much better in another. The stability of the earth, the fertility of the soil, the ever-varying behaviour of the sea, these are all things we understand well enough nowadays without the need to bring in giants and goddesses.

This view of myths is, however, a shallow one. The attempt to explain natural phenomena by personification may be dead, or moribund. But many of the motives which produced the myths of the Greek and Northern peoples remain active in us still. In consequence it is not enough to regard the old stories only as half-baked science. They were that, no doubt, among other things. When people used to talk about Zeus or Wotan as the thunder-maker, they certainly thought that in these terms the occurrence of thunderstorms could be explained, so to this extent the notion of Zeus played for them the part which the notion of atmospheric electricity does for us. Variations in natural phenomena, failure of the harvest or turbulence of the sea, were likewise to be understood in anthropomorphic terms, as the moods of divine agents, Ceres or Poseidon. But there was always something more to these myths. Zeus was not only the thunder-maker, he was also the Father of Men; and as such he played a very different role. For mere disinterested curiosity over unexplained phenomena would never have led people to talk of a "divine father," whether in Heaven or on Olympus: that has never been a purely scientific conception. So, though with the progress of science the motions of the sea and the stars and the growth of the corn have ceased to be for us the work of hidden hands, nevertheless some of the motives for myth-making are with us today as much as ever they were. Myths are with us, too. Our difficulty is, to know in which direction to look for the myths of the twentieth century, to recognize and unravel the non-scientific motives behind them, and to see these motives at work.

If we do think ourselves myth-free, when we are not, that is (I am suggesting) largely because the material from which we construct our myths is taken from the sciences themselves. The situation is the one we meet in those trickiest of crime stories, in which the detective himself turns out to have done the deed: he is the last man we suspect. There are of course other reasons too why we find it hard to recognize our own myths. To begin with, they are hard to spot, as our own fallacies are hard to spot, just because they are our own: fallacies, we are tempted to think, are the faults in *other* people's arguments, and myths the queer ideas people *used* to have about the universe. Again, we are inclined to suppose that myths must necessarily be anthropomorphic, and that personification is the unique road to myth. But this assumption is baseless: the myths of the twentieth century, as we shall see, are not so much anthropomorphic as mechanomorphic. And why, after all, should not the purposes of myth be served as effectively by picturing the world in terms of mythical machines as by invoking mythical personages? Still, in the main, it is because our contemporary myths are scientific ones that we fail to acknowledge them as being myths at all. The old picture of the world has been swept away; Poseidon and Wotan have suffered death by ridicule; and people not unnaturally look to the scientist for a substitute.

Therein lies the misunderstanding, for only in part were the ancient myths half-baked science, and only in part was their role an explanatory one. So far as this was so, we can reasonably look on the natural sciences as their descendants; but only so far. The other non-scientific motives behind them remain, and the sciences are not obliged to cater for these. The notion of atmospheric electricity, for example, was introduced to account in a scientific way for lightning and thunder, and to that extent displaced Zeus as the thunder-maker, but it was never intended to take over Zeus' role as the "divine father" as well. Rather, the two roles have been separated, so that thunderstorms are no longer regarded in the old way, as a topic for theology.

It is not enough, however, to suspect that there may be such "scientific myths": we must also know how to recognize them when we come across them. How are we to do this? Partly, I have argued, by seeing what sorts of question they are used to answer: if a conception, however scientific its birth or ancestry, is used in practice only as a way of dealing with non-scientific questions — whether ethical, philosophical or theological — then it is no longer following the trade of its forefathers, and has ceased itself to be a scientific term at all. Again, there are some terms of irreproachably scientific origin which begin after a time to live double lives: as well as their primary, scientific *métier* they acquire part-time jobs of another kind. If we find evidence of such duplicity, our suspicions will be confirmed.

This is a clue, but it is one which immediately raises further questions. How is it, for instance, that such a double life is possible? Scientists take so much care in defining their terms that serious ambiguities cannot, surely, remain: if the meaning of their terms were not clear, one would expect this to have its effect on their work — to lead, that is, to trouble within science itself. And in any case, if a scientist has been true to his declared method, and has introduced into his theories only those terms which he absolutely requires in order to explain the phenomena he has been studying, what room is there for equivocation?

The answer to this question is a double one, partly historical, partly logical. The idea of a science which contains nothing but what is forced on us by the phenomena we are studying is only an ideal: it is not, and never will be, an accomplished fact. As a matter of method, no doubt, scientists do develop and modify their theories and conceptions in just such ways as will (so far as they can see) best accommodate the phenomena; nor are they prepared to allow outside considerations to obstruct such developments as the phenomena require. But the theories they subscribe to as a result, whether in the sixth century B.C. or in the fifteenth or twentieth A.D., fall short of the purist's ideal for two reasons. To begin with, their historical origins are against them. Anyone can see the points of resemblance between the cosmology of Plato's *Timaeus* and the Near Eastern myths which it was intended to displace; and, though many of these residual elements of myth have since dropped out of our science, it is imprudent to point the finger of scorn at Plato (as Sarton does) until we have inquired whether this elimination has been completed. It is wiser to recognize that, as our scientific ideas develop, there will always be a tug-of-war between tradition and method: a scientist's *methods* may be completely empirical, yet his investigations will have no direction without the guidance of a pre-existing body of ideas, some of which may turn out under scrutiny to be survivals from surprisingly far back.

This factor may, as the centuries pass, be of less and less importance, but the other is of a permanent relevance. However much the sciences may eventually outgrow their historical swaddling-bands, there must always be something more to the framework of ideas which constitutes a theory than the bare recapitulation of the phenomena it is used to explain. The structure of a scientific theory may be built up entirely from the bricks of observation, but the exact position the bricks occupy depends on the layout of the scientist's conceptual scaffolding; and this element of scaffolding, which the scientist introduces himself, is always open to misinterpretation.

Neither of these factors is one which need affect the scientific value and validity of a theory. If a term like "evolution" comes to be used ambiguously — having both a pure biological use and an extended, philosophical or mythological use — this ambiguity is not one which will necessarily show up in a strictly biological argument. The aspects of the notion which are put to mythological use may not be ones that bear either way on any biological questions; and so long as they do not do so, the notion will preserve all its power within biology. Even to speak of ambiguity in this context may therefore be too strong. What we have rather is a choice between two interpretations of a term, a narrow one and a wide one: a narrow one, whose use and justification lie wholly within the natural sciences, and a wider, extended one, whose justification and use both lie in part elsewhere.

With this point in mind, we can clear out of the way one elementary misunderstanding. When I go on to argue that some familiar notion — The Running-Down Universe, for instance, or Evolution regarded as "the Cosmic Process" — is a scientific myth, I shall not be making a point which raises questions of a straightforward scientific kind. In particular, I shall not be casting any shadow of doubt either on the laws of thermo-dynamics, or on the doctrine that species have developed by variation and natural selection. There are, no doubt, plenty of people who still reject Darwin's theory even as biology. I am not one of them: in its essentials it seems to me among the finest and most firmly established products of biological thought. The claim that Evolution is sometimes treated as a myth must not, then, be misunderstood: it is quite distinct from any possible claim that, as a scientific theory, there is something dubious or unsound or even speculative about the Darwinian view of the origin of species.

People do, it is true, sometimes say "So-and-So is a myth," meaning only that the belief is untrue or unsound; and this might be said of Darwin's theory by an anti-evolutionist, as a contemptuous way of dis-missing it. But do not let us fall victims to this sort of loose expression. To use the word myth only as a term of abuse is to rob ourselves of a useful distinction. Not all out-dated scientific concepts were myths, nor vice versa — caloric, for instance, had no mythological significance. So, if we talk about scientific myths, let us do so strictly; in order to raise not scientific issues but logical ones. Granted that the theory of evolution or the laws of thermodynamics are all that a scientist can ask; granted that their position within biology and physics is as firmly established as it could be; if this may be allowed, just how much is accomplished? What sorts of conclusions are forced on us by our acceptance of these theories, and on which do they have no direct bearing? These are the questions we must ask. If we find that the theories are regularly invoked in support of conclusions of a kind to which, as scientific theories, they have no rele-vance; further, if these conclusions are of a sort with which mythologies have from the earliest times been concerned; then we can say with some justice, not that the theories themselves are 'only myths,' but rather that on these occasions their conceptions are being inflated into Scientific Myths.

Once again, then, how are we to recognize when a scientific term is being pressed into service of a non-scientific kind? The chief point to look out for is the following. When a technical term is introduced into a science, or an everyday word like force or energy is given a fresh, scientific application, it has a clearly defined place in a theory — a theory whose task it is to explain some limited range of phenomena. What gives the term a meaning for science is the part it plays in these explanations. One can think of such a term as a piece in a jig-saw puzzle; and, like such a piece, it loses most of its significance as soon as we try to make anything of it out of context. We can take the notion of universal gravitation (gravity, for short) as an example. When Newton introduced this idea, his purpose was a limited and tangible one: namely, to account for the motions of the planets, the comets and the moon in terms of the same laws of motion as held for terrestrial bodies. And when one says "account for," this means (as he himself took care to emphasize)[1] account in a mathematical way. For Newton's purposes, the term "gravity" acquired its meaning with the introduction of the inverse-square law; and this in its turn earned a place in physical theory because it could be used to work out how, in this or that situation, celestial or terrestrial bodies can be expected to move. As a piece of planetary dynamics, Newton's theory needed no other justification. He saw that in due course the theory might be amplified to deal with other phenomena, and the mode of action of gravity might thereby be discovered; but, he insisted, we must not jump to conclusions; and in any case his notion of "gravity" should not be taken as having any implications outside dynamical theory.

It is to some such modest but solid job that all scientific terms are put, "evolution," "entropy" and so on, quite as much as "gravity," and it is vital for the progress of science that their meaning should be limited in this way. It is just because the terms of the sciences are so well defined, and defined in a way which is closely tied down to the phenomena, that questions in science can be settled: only because this is so can scientists hope to answer definitely the questions that arise for them, by looking to see whether things actually happen in nature in the manner the theory suggests — in this way, they can usually come to agree upon one answer and reject the alternatives.

If this is forgotten, difficulties are created. Suppose we extend a carefully defined scientific term beyond the range of its theory, and use it in more ambitious but less tangible speculations, then there will be snags at once. For whereas before this was done one could check the soundness of

---

[1] Cf.: Newton, *Mathematical Principles of Natural Philosophy*, ed. F. Cajori (1934), pp. 550–1: "The System of the World," §2.

one's speculations against the facts, now things will be different: there will be no way of checking what is said by experiment or observation, and so, scientifically speaking, nothing to choose between one possible answer and another. And if this is so, if when a dispute arises there are now no conceivable observations to be made by which we can decide between the disputants, then there can be no question of either side in the dispute claiming for his doctrine the support of the theory concerned. The theory will be neutral between all such views.

Newton realized this also. It was not that he had any objection to wider speculations: as we know now, he spent a surprisingly large part of his time on natural theology, the interpretation of biblical prophecies and other non-scientific problems. But in these speculations he did not keep appealing to 'gravity.' The term had a clear meaning in dynamics, and it could play a part in theology only if it were given a radically different sense. When he came to expound his theory of gravitation, therefore, he put aside all wider questions, and the only rival views he bothered to consider were other genuinely physical ones — for instance, those of Descartes and his followers.

In Descartes's picture of the solar system one must think of the sun as surrounded by a vortex, and of the planets as carried round about it like floating chips: the idea of gravitational attraction played no part in the account at all. To this theory, Newton's reply was simple. It is not enough, he argued, for a theory to provide a vivid picture of the solar system: one must work out the mathematical consequences of the view in detail. If this is done for the vortex theory, you cannot, short of the most implausible and groundless assumptions, make it fit the facts. In the first place, to talk of a vortex at all suggests that the space between the planets is filled with some kind of celestial bath-water, whose motions carry the planets round with it. But there is no independent evidence at all for supposing the existence of this fluid: indeed there are several reasons for rejecting the supposition — such as the fact that comets travel right across the solar system without showing any sign either of resistance from the fluid or of the effects of the vortex on their line of travel, and the fact that the satellites of each planet, however far it is from the sun, travel round it in the same manner. Further, to make the vortex theory work quantitatively, one must assume not merely the existence of this wholly impalpable fluid: one must imagine it endowed with physical properties (already, alas, indetectable) which vary greatly from point to point in space. A theory expressed in such terms as these could be of little use to science. Newton's own theory, by contrast, would account for all the observed motions of the comets, the planets and their satellites exactly, and without such a mass of arbitrary assumptions.[2]

[2]Cf.: *op. cit.,* pp. 385–96: Bk. II, sect. ix.

No wonder Newton felt entitled to be satisfied with his theory. Yet it was assailed at once, from several directions. The followers of Descartes, of course, objected to the theory as physics; but others found wider reasons for attacking it. Leibniz, for instance, accused the doctrine of universal gravitation of being repugnant to common sense: to speak of the heavenly bodies as gravitating towards one another was, he said, "a strange fiction."[3] He further agreed with Berkeley in finding the implications of Newton's views impious, if not actually atheistical, for reasons which we do not now find it easy to accept.

These wider criticisms distressed Newton, but he did not spend much time answering them. Of course what he spoke of as gravity was an extension of the everyday, terrestrial notion, and must be understood as such. Leibniz might want to stand by the old sense of the term — the one enshrined in seventeenth-century "common sense"; but if one looked at the uses to which Newton put his extended notion, one would see how the extension could be justified.

Before his time, the notion of gravity had an application only to bodies on the earth — pick up a chair and it feels heavy (*gravis*), let it go and it falls (gravitates) to the ground. The heavenly bodies, by contrast, were quite unlike chairs. They moved in their stable orbits round the sun or kept their places in the more distant firmament — the notion of gravitation manifestly had no relevance to their behaviour. The hypothesis that the planets were *massive* was no doubt an intelligible one; that they were *heavy* would have been a less intelligible suggestion; and to talk of heavenly bodies falling or gravitating would have called to mind only the falling stars which appeared in spring and autumn to drop through the night sky, or the thunderbolts which from time to time would strike the earth and awe the superstitious.

Newton's theory changed all that. The regular motion of the planets round the sun, which his predecessors had so carefully described — this too, he declared, was an effect of "gravity" and a case of "gravitation," just as much as the weight of a chair or its fall to the ground when released. The view might seem paradoxical to some: the stars and planets have no visible means of support, yet they do not, like terrestrial bodies, fall to the ground for lack of it. But the view has a point, and a *scientific* point at that. One can represent the motions of the planets round the sun with a degree of accuracy exceeding anything detectable by observation in Newton's time by regarding them as freely moving bodies, acted on only by his "inverse square force": exactly the same force can be appealed to in explanation of those terrestrial phenomena which alone had hitherto been called gravitational. This was all that was in question in calling the motion of the planets "gravitational," or an effect of "gravity."

[3] Leibniz-Clarke correspondence: Leibniz's fifth letter, §35.

As for the question, whether the new theory was atheistical or not, even to ask this was to read things into the theory. What Newton had been doing was a piece of physics, as a result of which he had been able to explain in a mathematical way how the planets moved. The solar system, could, he thought, be none the less wonderful — none the less a tribute to the foresight of the Almighty — for our having gone thus far towards understanding it. Indeed he himself was inclined to think the opposite. To have shown that one set of mathematical principles underlay so many varied dynamical phenomena should (as he put it) "work with considering men for the belief of a Deity," so he could see nothing impious in the theory.[4] In any case, when it came to natural theology, what told in the balance was not the details of the theory. The precise form of his law of gravity could not therefore be relevant to any theological issue: the success of an inverse cube law would have been no less impressive than that of his own theory. All that was at issue, for theology, was the rationality of the universe, and this was something which any successful and comprehensive theory helped to vindicate. Meanwhile, there was plenty within physics to keep him busy — plenty of genuinely scientific questions, which one could hope to answer by reference to the telescope or an experiment. He had no time or inclination to defend the notion of gravitation from other people's misinterpretations.

From this example we can perhaps see what is liable to happen when scientific terms are used, not to explain anything, but for other purposes — for instance, as the raw material of myths. Technical scientific notions taken by themselves have, as we saw, about as much meaning as isolated pieces taken out of a jig-saw puzzle. If we try to do other things with them — for example, to build a comprehensive "world-view" of a philosophical kind from them — we are forgetting this fact, and treating them as though they were pieces of a single, cosmic jig-saw. This has two unfortunate consequences. First, you cannot get pieces taken from different puzzles to fit together at all except by distorting them; and in the second place, if one man forces them together in one way and one in another, nobody will be able to say that one or the other of the pictures so produced is, scientifically speaking, the "right" one.

These difficulties arise again when physical or biological theories are appealed to in an attempt to solve problems in, for instance, ethics or political theory. To begin with, all the scientific terms used get distorted in the process, and no longer keep the clear meaning they have in science proper: this fact alone shows the gulf between scientific myths and the theories whose concepts they exploit. Furthermore, when two people appeal to the same scientific theory as backing for different "world-views" or

---

[4] Cf. his letters to Richard Bentley, and the General Scholium added to the third edition of the *Mathematical Principles*, pp. 543–7.

different political doctrines, how can we even set about choosing between them? Within science, we can at any rate prove our views in practice. But when we put scientific terms to non-scientific uses, this, the chief merit of a scientific approach, is lost. For all that experiment or observation can show, one scientific myth is as good as another.

WILLIAM K. CLIFFORD

On the Aims and Instruments
of Scientific Thought

William Kingdom Clifford was among the most imaginative Victorian mathematicians, anticipating many parts of physics and mathematics. Although he gave this talk to the British Association for the Advancement of Science a century ago, very few ideas in it need be modified in the light of later developments.

It may have occurred (and very naturally too) to such as have had the curiosity to read the title of this lecture,[1] that it must necessarily be a very dry and difficult subject; interesting to very few, intelligible to still fewer, and, above all, utterly incapable of adequate treatment within the limits of a discourse like this. It is quite true that a complete setting-forth of my subject would require a comprehensive treatise on logic, with incidental discussion of the main questions of metaphysics; that it would deal with ideas demanding close study for their apprehension, and investigations requiring a peculiar taste to relish them. It is not my intention now to present you with such a treatise.

The British Association, like the world in general, contains three classes of persons. In the first place, it contains scientific thinkers; that is to say, persons whose thoughts have very frequently the characters which I shall presently describe. Secondly, it contains persons who are engaged in work upon what are called scientific subjects, but who in general do not, and are not expected to, think about these subjects in a scientific manner. Lastly, it contains persons who suppose that their work and their thoughts are unscientific, but who would like to know something about the business of the other two classes aforesaid. Now, to any one who belonging to one of these classes considers either of the other two, it will be apparent that there is a certain gulf between him and them; that he does not quite

W. K. Clifford. *Lectures and Essays.* (Macmillan, London, 1886.) Reference footnotes have been omitted.

[1] A Lecture delivered before the members of the British Association, at Brighton, on August 19, 1872.

understand them, nor they him; and that an opportunity for sympathy and comradeship is lost through this want of understanding. It is this gulf that I desire to bridge over, to the best of my power. That the scientific thinker may consider his business in relation to the great life of mankind; that the noble army of practical workers may recognize their fellowship with the outer world, and the spirit which must guide both; that this so-called outer world may see in the work of science only the putting in evidence of all that is excellent in its own work — may feel that the kingdom of science is within it: these are the objects of the present discourse. And they compel me to choose such portions of my vast subject as shall be intelligible to all, while they ought at least to command an interest universal, personal, and profound.

In the first place, then, what is meant by scientific thought? You may have heard some of it expressed in the various Sections this morning. You have probably also heard expressed in the same places a great deal of unscientific thought; notwithstanding that it was about mechanical energy, or about hydrocarbons, or about eocene deposits, or about malacopterygii. For scientific thought does not mean thought about scientific subjects with long names. There are no scientific subjects. The subject of science is the human universe; that is to say, everything that is, or has been, or may be related to man. Let us then, taking several topics in succession, endeavour to make out in what cases thought about them is scientific, and in what cases not.

Ancient astronomers observed that the relative motions of the sun and moon recurred all over again in the same order about every nineteen years. They were thus enabled to predict the time at which eclipses would take place. A calculator at one of our observatories can do a great deal more than this. Like them, he makes use of past experience to predict the future; but he knows of a great number of other cycles besides that one of the nineteen years, and takes account of all of them; and he can tell about the solar eclipse of six years hence exactly when it will be visible, and how much of the sun's surface will be covered at each place, and, to a second, at what time of day it will begin and finish there. This prediction involves technical skill of the highest order; but it does not involve scientific thought, as any astronomer will tell you.

By such calculations the places of the planet Uranus at different times of the year had been predicted and set down. The predictions were not fulfilled. Then arose Adams, and from these errors in the prediction he calculated the place of an entirely new planet, that had never yet been suspected; and you all know how the new planet was actually found in that place. Now this prediction does involve scientific thought, as anyone who has studied it will tell you.

Here then are two cases of thought about the same subject, both predicting events by the application of previous experience, yet we say one is *technical* and the other *scientific*.

Now let us take an example from the building of bridges and roofs. When an opening is to be spanned over by a material construction, which must bear a certain weight without bending enough to injure itself, there are two forms in which this construction can be made, the arch and the chain. Every part of an arch is compressed or pushed by the other parts; every part of a chain is in a state of tension, or is pulled by the other parts. In many cases these forms are united. A girder consists of two main pieces or booms, of which the upper one acts as an arch and is compressed, while the lower one acts as a chain and is pulled; and this is true even when both the pieces are quite straight. They are enabled to act in this way by being tied together, or braced, as it is called, by cross pieces, which you must often have seen. Now suppose that any good practical engineer makes a bridge or roof upon some approved pattern which has been made before. He designs the size and shape of it to suit the opening which has to be spanned; selects his material according to the locality; assigns the strength which must be given to the several parts of the structure according to the load which it will have to bear. There is a great deal of thought in the making of this design, whose success is predicted by the application of previous experience; it requires technical skill of a very high order; but it is not scientific thought. On the other hand, Mr. Fleeming Jenkin designs a roof consisting of two arches braced together, instead of an arch and a chain braced together; and although this form is quite different from any known structure, yet before it is built he assigns with accuracy the amount of material that must be put into every part of the structure in order to make it bear the required load, and this prediction may be trusted with perfect security. What is the natural comment on this? Why, that Mr. Fleeming Jenkin is a scientific engineer.

Now it seems to me that the difference between scientific and merely technical thought, not only in these but in all other instances which I have considered, is just this: Both of them make use of experience to direct human action; but while technical thought or skill enables a man to deal with the same circumstances that he has met with before, scientific thought enables him to deal with different circumstances that he has never met with before. But how can experience of one thing enable us to deal with another quite different thing? To answer this question we shall have to consider more closely the nature of scientific thought.

Let us take another example. You know that if you make a dot on a piece of paper, and then hold a piece of Iceland spar over it, you will see not one dot but two. A mineralogist, by measuring the angles of a crystal, can tell you whether or no it possesses this property without looking through it. He requires no scientific thought to do that. But Sir William

Rowan Hamilton, the late Astronomer-Royal of Ireland, knowing these facts and also the explanation of them which Fresnel had given, thought about the subject, and he predicted that by looking through certain crystals in a particular direction we should see not two dots but a continuous circle. Mr. Lloyd made the experiment, and saw the circle, a result which had never been even suspected. This has always been considered one of the most signal instances of scientific thought in the domain of physics. It is most distinctly an application of experience gained under certain circumstances to entirely different circumstances.

Now suppose that the night before coming down to Brighton you had dreamed of a railway accident caused by the engine getting frightened at a flock of sheep and jumping suddenly back over all the carriages; the result of which was that your head was unfortunately cut off, so that you had to put it in your hat-box and take it back home to be mended. There are, I fear, many persons even at this day, who would tell you that after such a dream it was unwise to travel by railway to Brighton. This is a proposal that you should take experience gained while you are asleep, when you have no common sense experience about a phantom railway, and apply it to guide you when you are awake and have common sense, in your dealings with a real railway. And yet this proposal is not dictated by scientific thought.

Now let us take the great example of Biology. I pass over the process of classification, which itself requires a great deal of scientific thought; in particular when a naturalist who has studied and monographed a fauna or a flora rather than a family is able at once to pick out the distinguishing characters required for the subdivision of an order quite new to him. Suppose that we possess all this minute and comprehensive knowledge of plants and animals and intermediate organisms, their affinities and differences, their structures and functions — a vast body of experience, collected by incalculable labour and devotion. Then comes Mr. Herbert Spencer: he takes that experience of life which is not human, which is apparently stationary, going on in exactly the same way from year to year, and he applies that to tell us how to deal with the changing characters of human nature and human society. How is it that experience of this sort, vast as it is, can guide us in a matter so different from itself? How does scientific thought, applied to the development of a kangaroo foetus or the movement of the sap in exogens, make prediction possible for the first time in that most important of all sciences, the relations of man with man?

In the dark or unscientific ages men had another way of applying experience to altered circumstances. They believed, for example, that the plant called Jew's-ear, which does bear a certain resemblance to the human ear, was a useful cure for diseases of that organ. This doctrine of "signatures," as it was called, exercised an enormous influence on the medicine of the time. I need hardly tell you that it is hopelessly unscientific; yet it agrees with those other examples that we have been considering in this particular; that it applies experience about the shape of a plant — which is one circumstance connected with it — to dealings with its medicinal properties, which are other and different circumstances. Again, suppose that you had been frightened by a thunderstorm on land, or your heart had failed you in a storm at sea; if any one then told you that in consequence of this you should always cultivate an unpleasant sensation in the pit of your stomach, till you took delight in it, that you should regulate your sane and sober life by the sensations of a moment of unreasoning terror: this advice would not be an example of scientific thought. Yet it would be an application of past experience to new and different circumstances.

But you will already have observed what is the additional clause that we must add to our definition in order to describe scientific thought and that only. The step between experience about animals and dealings with changing humanity is the law of evolution. The step from errors in the calculated places of Uranus to the existence of Neptune is the law of gravitation. The step from the observed behaviour of crystals to conical refraction is made up of laws of light and geometry. The step from old bridges to new ones is the laws of elasticity and the strength of materials.

The step, then, from past experience to new circumstances must be made in accordance with an observed uniformity in the order of events. This uniformity has held good in the past in certain places; if it should also hold good in the future and in other places, then, being combined with our experience of the past, it enables us to predict the future, and to know what is going on elsewhere; so that we are able to regulate our conduct in accordance with this knowledge.

The aim of scientific thought, then, is to apply past experience to new circumstances; the instrument is an observed uniformity in the course of events. By the use of this instrument it gives us information transcending our experience, it enables us to infer things that we have not seen from things that we have seen; and the evidence for the truth of that information depends on our supposing that the uniformity holds good beyond our experience. I now want to consider this uniformity a little more closely; to show how the character of scientific thought and the force of its inferences depend upon the character of the uniformity of Nature. I cannot of course tell you all that is known of this character without writing an encyclopædia; but I shall confine myself to two points of it about which it seems to me that just now there is something to be said. I want to find out what we mean when we say that the uniformity of Nature is *exact;* and what we mean when we say that it is *reasonable.*

When a student is first introduced to those sciences which have come under the dominion of mathematics, a new and wonderful aspect of Nature bursts upon his view. He has been accustomed to regard things as essentially more or less vague. All the facts that he has hitherto known have been expressed qualitatively, with a little allowance for error on either side. Things which are let go fall to the ground. A very observant man may know also that they fall faster as they go along. But our student is shown that, after falling for one second in a vacuum, a body is going at the rate of thirty-two feet per second, that after falling for two seconds it is going twice as fast, after going two and a half seconds two and a half times as fast. If he makes the experiment, and finds a single inch per second too much or too little in the rate, one of two things must have happened: either the law of falling bodies has been wrongly stated, or the experiment is not accurate—there is some mistake. He finds reason to think that the latter is always the case; the more carefully he goes to work, the more of the error turns out to belong to the experiment. Again, he may know that water consists of two gases, oxygen and hydrogen, combined; but he now learns that two pints of steam at a temperature of 150° Centigrade will always make two pints of hydrogen and one pint of oxygen at the same temperature, all of them being pressed as much as the atmosphere is pressed. If he makes the experiment and gets rather more or less than a pint of oxygen, is the law disproved? No; the steam was impure, or there was some mistake. Myriads of analyses attest the law of combining volumes; the more carefully they are made, the more nearly they coincide with it. The aspects of the faces of a crystal are connected together by a geometrical law, by which, four of them being given, the rest can be found. The place of a planet at a given time is calculated by the law of gravitation; if it is half a second wrong, the fault is in the instrument, the observer, the clock, or the law; now, the more observations are made, the more of this fault is brought home to the instrument, the observer, and the clock. It is no wonder, then, that our student, contemplating these and many like instances, should be led to say, "I have been short-sighted; but I have now put on the spectacles of science which Nature had prepared for my eyes; I see that things have definite outlines, that the world is ruled by exact and rigid mathematical laws; καὶ σύ, θεός, γεωμετρεῖς." It is our business to consider whether he is right in so concluding. Is the uniformity of Nature absolutely exact, or only more exact than our experiments?

At this point we have to make a very important distinction. There are two ways in which a law may be inaccurate. The first way is exemplified by that law of Galileo which I mentioned just now: that a body falling *in vacuo* acquires equal increase in velocity in equal times. No matter how many feet per second it is going, after an interval of a second it will be going thirty-two *more* feet per second. We now know that this rate of increase is not exactly the same at different heights, that it depends upon the distance of the body from the centre of the earth; so that the law is only approximate; instead of the increase of velocity being exactly *equal* in equal times, it itself increases very slowly as the body falls. We know also that this variation of the law from the truth is *too small to be perceived* by direct observation on the change of velocity. But suppose we have invented means for observing this, and have verified that the increase of velocity is inversely as the squared distance from the earth's centre. Still the law is not accurate; for the earth does not attract accurately towards her centre, and the direction of attraction is continually varying with the motion of the sea; the body will not even fall in a straight line. The sun and the planets, too, especially the moon, will produce deviations; yet the sum of all these errors will escape our new process of observation, by being a great deal smaller than the necessary errors of that observation. But when these again have been allowed for, there is still the influence of the stars. In this case, however, we only give up one exact law for another. It may still be held that if the effect of every particle of matter in the universe on the falling body were calculated according to the law of gravitation, the body would move exactly as this calculation required. And if it were objected that the body must be slightly magnetic or diamagnetic, while there are magnets not an infinite way off; that a very minute repulsion, even at sensible distances, accompanies the attraction; it might be replied that these phenomena are themselves subject to exact laws, and that when *all* the laws have been taken into account, the actual motion will exactly correspond with the calculated motion.

I suppose there is hardly a physical student (unless he has specially considered the matter) who would not at once assent to the statement I have just made; that if we knew all about it, Nature would be found universally subject to exact numerical laws. But let us just consider for another moment what this means.

The word "exact" has a practical and a theoretical meaning. When a grocer weighs you out a certain quantity of sugar very carefully, and says it is exactly a pound, he means that the difference between the mass of the sugar and that of the pound weight he employs is too small to be detected by his scales. If a chemist had made a special investigation, wishing to be as accurate as he could, and told you this was exactly a pound of sugar, he would mean that the mass of the sugar differed from that of a certain standard piece of platinum by a quantity too small to be detected by *his* means of weighing, which are a thousandfold more accurate than the grocer's. But what would a mathematician mean, if he made the same statement? He would mean this. Suppose the mass of the standard pound to be represented by a length, say a foot, measured on a certain line; so

that half a pound would be represented by six inches, and so on. And let
the difference between the mass of the sugar and that of the standard
pound be drawn upon the same line to the same scale. Then, if that difference were magnified an infinite number of times, it would still be invisible. This is the theoretical meaning of exactness; the practical meaning
is only very close approximation; *how* close, depends upon the circumstances. The knowledge then of an exact law in the theoretical sense
would be equivalent to an infinite observation. I do not say that such
knowledge is impossible to man; but I do say that it would be absolutely
different in kind from any knowledge that we possess at present.

I shall be told, no doubt, that we do possess a great deal of knowledge
of this kind, in the form of geometry and mechanics; and that
it is just the example of these sciences that has led men to look for
exactness in other quarters. If this had been said to me in the last century,
I should not have known what to reply. But it happens that about the
beginning of the present century the foundations of geometry were criti-
cised independently by two mathematicians, Lobatschewsky and the immortal Gauss, whose results have been extended and generalized more
recently by Riemann and Helmholtz. And the conclusion to which these
investigations lead is that, although the assumptions which were very
properly made by the ancient geometers are practically exact — that is to
say, more exact than experiment can be — for such finite things as we
have to deal with, and such portions of space as we can reach; yet the
truth of them for very much larger things, or very much smaller things, or
parts of space which are at present beyond our reach, is a matter to be
decided by experiment, when its powers are considerably increased. I
want to make as clear as possible the real state of this question at present,
because it is often supposed to be a question of words or metaphysics,
whereas it is a very distinct and simple question of fact. I am supposed to
know then that the three angles of a rectilinear triangle are exactly equal
to two right angles. Now suppose that three points are taken in space,
distant from one another as far as the Sun is from *a* Centauri, and that
the shortest distances between these points are drawn so as to form a
triangle. And suppose the angles of this triangle to be very accurately
measured and added together; this can at present be done so accurately
that the error shall certainly be less than one minute, less therefore than
the five-thousandth part of a right angle. Then I do not know that this
sum would differ at all from two right angles; but also I do not know that
the difference would be less than ten degrees, or the ninth part of a right
angle.[2] And I have reasons for not knowing.

[2] Assuming that parallax observations prove the deviation less than half a second for a
triangle whose vertex is at the star and base a diameter of the earth's orbit.

This example is exceedingly important as showing the connection between exactness and universality. It is found that the deviation if it exists
must be nearly proportional to the area of the triangle. So that the error
in the case of a triangle whose sides are a mile long would be obtained by
dividing that in the case I have just been considering by four hundred
quadrillions; the result must be a quantity inconceivably small, which no
experiment could detect. But between this inconceivably small error and
no error at all, there is fixed an enormous gulf; the gulf between practical
and theoretical exactness, and, what is even more important, the gulf
between what is practically universal and what is theoretically universal. I
say that a law is practically universal which is more exact than experiment
for all cases that might be got at by such experiments as we can make.
We assume this kind of universality, and we find that it pays us to assume
it. But a law would be theoretically universal if it were true of all cases
whatever; and this is what we do not know of any law at all.

I said there were two ways in which a law might be inexact. There is a
law of gases which asserts that when you compress a perfect gas the
pressure of the gas increases exactly in the proportion in which the volume diminishes. Exactly; that is to say, the law is more accurate than the
experiment, and experiments are corrected by means of the law. But it so
happens that this law has been explained; we know precisely what it is
that happens when a gas is compressed. We know that a gas consists of a
vast number of separate molecules, rushing about in all directions with all
manner of velocities, but so that the mean velocity of the molecules of air
in this room, for example, is about twenty miles a minute. The pressure of
the gas on any surface with which it is in contact is nothing more than the
impact of these small particles upon it. On any surface large enough to be
seen there are millions of these impacts in a second. If the space in which
the gas is confined be diminished, the average rate at which the impacts
take place will be increased in the same proportion; and because of the
enormous number of them, the actual rate is always exceedingly close to
the average. But the law is one of statistics; its accuracy depends on the
enormous numbers involved; and so, from the nature of the case, its
exactness cannot be theoretical or absolute.

Nearly all the laws of gases have received these statistical explanations;
electric and magnetic attraction and repulsion have been treated in a
similar manner; and an hypothesis of this sort has been suggested even for
the law of gravity. On the other hand the manner in which the molecules
of a gas interfere with each other proves that they repel one another
inversely as the fifth power of the distance;[3] so that we here find at the
basis of a statistical explanation a law which has the form of theoretical

---

[3] [This statement of the law has since been abandoned.]

exactness. Which of these forms is to win? It seems to me again that we do not know, and that the recognition of our ignorance is the surest way to get rid of it.

The world in general has made just the remark that I have attributed to a fresh student of the applied sciences. As the discoveries of Galileo, Kepler, Newton, Dalton, Cavendish, Gauss, displayed ever new phenomena following mathematical laws, the theoretical exactness of the physical universe was taken for granted. Now, when people are hopelessly ignorant of a thing, they quarrel about the source of their knowledge. Accordingly many maintained that we know these exact laws by intuition. These said always one true thing, that we did not know them from experience. Others said that they were really given in the facts, and adopted ingenious ways of hiding the gulf between the two. Others again deduced from transcendental considerations sometimes the laws themselves, and sometimes what through imperfect information they supposed to be the laws. But more serious consequences arose when these conceptions derived from Physics were carried over into the field of Biology. Sharp lines of division were made between kingdoms and classes and orders; an animal was described as a miracle to the vegetable world; specific differences which are practically permanent within the range of history were regarded as permanent through all time; a sharp line was drawn between organic and inorganic matter. Further investigation, however, has shown that accuracy had been prematurely attributed to the science, and has filled up all the gulfs and gaps that hasty observers had invented. The animal and vegetable kingdoms have a debatable ground between them, occupied by beings that have the characters of both and yet belong distinctly to neither. Classes and orders shade into one another all along their common boundary. Specific differences turn out to be the work of time. The line dividing organic matter from inorganic, if drawn to-day, must be moved to-morrow to another place; and the chemist will tell you that the distinction has now no place in his science except in a technical sense for the convenience of studying carbon compounds by themselves. In Geology the same tendency gave birth to the doctrine of distinct periods, marked out by the character of the strata deposited in them all over the sea; a doctrine than which, perhaps, no ancient cosmogony has been further from the truth, or done more harm to the progress of science. Refuted many years ago by Mr. Herbert Spencer, it has now fairly yielded to an attack from all sides at once, and may be left in peace.

When then we say that the uniformity which we observe in the course of events is exact and universal, we mean no more than this: that we are able to state general rules which are far more exact than direct experiment, and which apply to all cases that we are at present likely to come across. It is important to notice, however, the effect of such exactness as we observe upon the nature of inference. When a telegram arrived stating that Dr. Livingstone had been found by Mr. Stanley, what was the process by which you inferred the finding of Dr. Livingstone from the appearance of the telegram? You assumed over and over again the existence of uniformity in nature. That the newspapers had behaved as they generally do in regard to telegraphic messages; that the clerks had followed the known laws of the action of clerks; that electricity had behaved in the cable exactly as it behaves in the laboratory; that the actions of Mr. Stanley were related to his motives by the same uniformities that affect the actions of other men; that Dr. Livingstone's handwriting conformed to the curious rule by which an ordinary man's handwriting may be recognised as having persistent characteristics even at different periods of his life. But you had a right to be much more sure about some of these inferences than about others. The law of electricity was known with practical exactness, and the conclusions derived from it were the surest things of all. The law about the handwriting, belonging to a portion of physiology which is unconnected with consciousness, was known with less, but still with considerable accuracy. But the laws of human action in which consciousness is concerned are still so far from being completely analysed and reduced to an exact form that the inferences which you made by their help were felt to have only a provisional force. It is possible that by and by, when psychology has made enormous advances and become an exact science, we may be able to give to testimony the sort of weight which we give to the inferences of physical science. It will then be possible to conceive a case which will show how completely the whole process of inference depends on our assumption of uniformity. Suppose that testimony, having reached the ideal force I have imagined, were to assert that a certain river runs uphill. You could infer nothing at all. The arm of inference would be paralysed, and the sword of truth broken in its grasp; and reason could only sit down and wait until recovery restored her limb, and further experience gave her new weapons.

I want in the next place to consider what we mean when we say that the uniformity which we have observed in the course of events is *reasonable* as well as exact.

No doubt the first form of this idea was suggested by the marvellous adaptation of certain natural structures to special functions. The first impression of those who studied comparative anatomy was that every part of the animal frame was fitted with extraordinary completeness for the work that it had to do. I say extraordinary, because at the time the most familiar examples of this adaptation were manufactures produced by human ingenuity; and the completeness and minuteness of natural adaptations were seen to be far in advance of these. The mechanism of limbs and joints was seen to be adapted, far better than any existing ironwork, to those motions and combinations of motion which were most useful to the particular organisms. The beautiful and complicated apparatus of sensation caught up indications from the surrounding medium, sorted them, analysed them, and transmitted the results to the brain in a manner with which, at the time I am speaking of, no artificial contrivance could compete. Hence the belief grew amongst physiologists that every structure which they found must have its function and subserve some useful purpose; a belief which was not without its foundation in fact, and which certainly (as Dr. Whewell remarks) has done admirable service in promoting the growth of physiology. Like all beliefs found successful in one subject, it was carried over into another, of which a notable example is given in the speculations of Count Rumford about the physical properties of water. Pure water attains its greatest density at a temperature of about 39½ ° Fahrenheit; it expands and becomes lighter whether it is cooled or heated, so as to alter that temperature. Hence it was concluded that water in this state must be at the bottom of the sea, and that by such means the sea was kept from freezing all through; as it was supposed must happen if the greatest density had been that of ice. Here then was a substance whose properties were eminently adapted to secure an end essential to the maintenance of life upon the earth. In short, men came to the conclusion that the order of nature was reasonable in the sense that everything was adapted to some good end.

Further consideration, however, has led men out of that conclusion in two different ways. First, it was seen that the facts of the case had been wrongly stated. Cases were found of wonderfully complicated structures that served no purpose at all; like the teeth of that whale of which you heard in Section D the other day, or of the Dugong, which has a horny palate covering them all up and used instead of them; like the eyes of the unborn mole, that are never used, though perfect as those of a mouse until the skull opening closes up, cutting them off from the brain, when they dry up and become incapable of use; like the outsides of your own ears, which are absolutely of no use to you. And when human contrivances were move advanced it became clear that the natural adaptations were subject to criticism. The eye, regarded as an optical instrument of human manufacture, was thus described by Helmholtz — the physiologist who learned physics for the sake of his physiology, and mathematics for the sake of his physics, and is now in the first rank of all three. He said, "If an optician sent me that as an instrument, I should send it back to him with grave reproaches for the carelessness of his work, and demand the return of my money."

The extensions of the doctrine into Physics were found to be still more at fault. That remarkable property of pure water, which was to have kept the sea from freezing, does not belong to salt water, of which the sea itself is composed. It was found, in fact, that the idea of a reasonable adaptation of means to ends, useful as it had been in its proper sphere, could yet not be called universal, or applied to the order of nature as a whole.

Secondly, this idea has given way because it has been superseded by a higher and more general idea of what is reasonable, which has the advantage of being applicable to a large portion of physical phenomena besides. Both the adaptation and the non-adaptation which occur in organic structures have been *explained*. The scientific thought of Dr. Darwin, of Mr. Herbert Spencer, and of Mr. Wallace, has described that hitherto unknown process of adaptation as consisting of perfectly well-known and familiar processes. There are two kinds of these: the direct processes, in which the physical changes required to produce a structure are worked out by the very actions for which that structure becomes adapted — as the backbone or notochord has been modified from generation to generation by the bendings which it has undergone; and the indirect processes included under the head of Natural Selection — the reproduction of children slightly different from their parents, and the survival of those which are best fitted to hold their own in the struggle for existence. Naturalists might give you some idea of the rate at which we are getting explanations of the evolution of all parts of animals and plants — the growth of the skeleton, of the nervous system and its mind, of leaf and flower. But what then do we mean by *explanation?*

We were considering just now an explanation of a law of gases — the law according to which pressure increases in the same proportion in which volume diminishes. The explanation consisted in supposing that a gas is made up of a vast number of minute particles always flying about and striking against one another, and then showing that the rate of impact of such a crowd of particles on the sides of the vessel containing them would vary exactly as the pressure is found to vary. Suppose the vessel to have parallel sides, and that there is only one particle rushing backwards and forwards between them; then it is clear that if we bring the sides together to half the distance, the particle will hit each of them twice as often, or the pressure will be doubled. Now it turns out that this would be just as true for millions of particles as for one, and when they are flying in all directions instead of only in one direction and its opposite. Observe now; it is a perfectly well-known and familiar thing that a body should strike against an opposing surface and bound off again; and it is a mere everyday occurrence that what has only half so far to go should be back in half the time; but that pressure should be strictly proportional to density is a comparatively strange, unfamiliar phenomenon. The explanation describes the unknown and unfamiliar as being made up of the known and the familiar; and this, it seems to me, is the true meaning of explanation.[4]

Here is another instance. If small pieces of camphor are dropped into water, they will begin to spin round and swim about in a most marvellous way. Mr. Tomlinson gave, I believe, the explanation of this. We must observe, to begin with, that every liquid has a skin which holds it; you can see that to be true in the case of a drop, which looks as if it were held in a bag. But the tension of this skin is greater in some liquids than in others; and it is greater in camphor and water than in pure water. When the camphor is dropped into water it begins to dissolve and get surrounded with camphor and water instead of water. If the fragment of camphor were exactly symmetrical, nothing more would happen; the tension would be greater in its immediate neighbourhood, but no motion would follow. The camphor, however, is irregular in shape; it dissolves more on one side than the other; and consequently gets pulled about, because the tension of the skin is greater where the camphor is most dissolved. Now it is probable that this is not nearly so satisfactory an explanation to you as it was to me when I was first told of it; and for this reason. By that time I was already perfectly familiar with the notion of a skin upon the surface of liquids, and I had been taught by means of it to work out problems in capillarity. The explanation was therefore a description of the unknown phenomenon which I did not know how to deal with as made up of known phenomena which I did know how to deal with. But to many of you possibly the liquid skin may seem quite as strange and unaccountable as the motion of camphor on water.

And this brings me to consider the source of the pleasure we derive from an explanation. By known and familiar I mean that which we know how to deal with, either by action in the ordinary sense, or by active thought. When therefore that which we do not know how to deal with is described as made up of things that we do know how to deal with, we have that sense of increased power which is the basis of all higher pleasures. Of course we may afterwards by association come to take pleasure in explanation for its own sake. Are we then to say that the observed order of events is reasonable, in the sense that all of it admits of explanation? That a process may be capable of explanation, it must break up into simpler constituents which are already familiar to us. Now, first, the process may itself be simple, and not break up; secondly, it may break up into elements which are as unfamiliar and impracticable as the original process.

It is an explanation of the moon's motion to say that she is a falling

---

[4] This view differs from those of Mr. J. S. Mill and Mr. Herbert Spencer in requiring every explanation to contain an addition to our knowledge about the thing explained. Both those writers regard subsumption under a general law as a species of explanation. See also Ferrier's *Remains*, vol. ii. p. 436.

body, only she is going so fast and is so far off that she falls quite round to the other side of the earth, instead of hitting it; and so goes on for ever. But it is no explanation to say that a body falls because of gravitation. That means that the motion of the body may be resolved into a motion of every one of its particles towards every one of the particles of the earth, with an acceleration inversely as the square of the distance between them. But this attraction of two particles must always, I think, be less familiar than the original falling body, however early the children of the future begin to read their Newton. Can the attraction itself be explained? Le Sage said that there is an everlasting hail of innumerable small ether-particles from all sides, and that the two material particles shield each other from this and so get pushed together. This is an explanation; it may or may not be a true one. The attraction may be an ultimate simple fact; or it may be made up of simpler facts utterly unlike anything that we know at present; and in either of these cases there is no explanation. We have no right to conclude, then, that the order of events is always capable of being explained.

There is yet another way in which it is said that Nature is reasonable; namely, inasmuch as every effect has a cause. What do we mean by this?

In asking this question, we have entered upon an appalling task. The word represented by "cause" has sixty-four meanings in Plato and forty-eight in Aristotle. These were men who liked to know as near as might be what they meant; but how many meanings it has had in the writings of the myriads of people who have not tried to know what they meant by it will, I hope, never be counted. It would not only be the height of presumption in me to attempt to fix the meaning of a word which has been used by so grave authority in so many and various senses; but it would seem a thankless task to do that once more which has been done so often at sundry times and in divers manners before. And yet without this we cannot determine what we mean by saying that the order of nature is reasonable. I shall evade the difficulty by telling you Mr. Grote's opinion. You come to a scarecrow and ask, what is the cause of this? You find that a man made it to frighten the birds. You go away and say to yourself, "Everything resembles this scarecrow. Everything has a purpose." And from that day the word "cause" means for you what Aristotle meant by "final cause." Or you go into a hairdresser's shop, and wonder what turns the wheel to which the rotatory brush is attached. On investigating other parts of the premises, you find a man working away at a handle. Then you go away and say, "Everything is like that wheel. If I investigated enough, I should always find a man at a handle." And the man at the handle, or whatever corresponds to him, is from henceforth known to you as "cause."

And so generally. When you have made out any sequence of events to your entire satisfaction, so that you know all about it, the laws involved being so familiar that you seem to see how the beginning must have been followed by the end, then you apply that as a simile to all other events whatever, and your idea of cause is determined by it. Only when a case arises, as it always must, to which the simile will not apply, you do not confess to yourself that it was only a simile and need not apply to everything, but you say, "The cause of that event is a mystery which must remain for ever unknown to me." On equally just grounds the nervous system of my umbrella is a mystery which must remain for ever unknown to me. My umbrella has no nervous system; and the event to which your simile did not apply has no cause in your sense of the word. When we say then that every effect has a cause, we mean that every event is connected with something in a way that might make somebody call that the cause of it. But I, at least, have never yet seen any single meaning of the word that could be fairly applied to the *whole* order of nature.

From this remark I cannot even except an attempt recently made by Mr. Bain to give the word a universal meaning, though I desire to speak of that attempt with the greatest respect. Mr. Bain wishes to make the word "cause" hang on in some way to what we call the law of energy; but though I speak with great diffidence I do think a careful consideration will show that the introduction of this word "cause" can only bring confusion into a matter which is distinct and clear enough to those who have taken the trouble to understand what energy means. It would be impossible to explain that this evening; but I may mention that "energy" is a technical term out of mathematical physics, which requires of most men a good deal of careful study to understand it accurately.

Let us pass on to consider, with all the reverence which it demands, another opinion held by great numbers of the philosophers who have lived in the Brightening Ages of Europe; the opinion that at the basis of the natural order there is something which we can know to be *unreasonable*, to evade the processes of human thought. The opinion is set forth first by Kant, so far as I know, in the form of his famous doctrine of the antinomies or contradictions, a later form[5] of which I will endeavour to explain to you. It is said, then, that space must either be infinite or have a boundary. Now you cannot conceive infinite space; and you cannot conceive that there should be any end to it. Here, then, are two things, one of which must be true, while each of them is inconceivable; so that our thoughts about space are hedged in, as it were, by a contradiction. Again, it is said that matter must either be infinitely divisible, or must consist of small particles incapable of further division. Now you cannot conceive a

[5] That of Mr. Herbert Spencer, *First Principles.* I believe Kant himself would have admitted that the antinomies do not exist for the empiricist. (Much less does he say that either of a pair of antinomies must be true. The real Kantian position is that both assertions are illegitimate.)

piece of matter divided into an infinite number of parts, while, on the other hand, you cannot conceive a piece of matter, however small, which absolutely cannot be divided into two pieces; for, however great the forces are which join the parts of it together, you can imagine stronger forces able to tear it in pieces. Here, again, there are two statements, one of which must be true, while each of them is separately inconceivable; so that our thoughts about matter also are hedged in by a contradiction. There are several other cases of the same thing, but I have selected these two as instructive examples. And the conclusion to which philosophers were led by the contemplation of them was that on every side, when we approach the limits of existence, a contradiction must stare us in the face. The doctrine has been developed and extended by the great successors of Kant; and this unreasonable, or unknowable, which is also called the absolute and the unconditioned, has been set forth in various ways as that which we know to be the true basis of all things. As I said before, I approach this doctrine with all the reverence which should be felt for that which has guided the thoughts of so many of the wisest of mankind. Nevertheless I shall endeavour to show that in these cases of supposed contradiction there is always something which we do not know now, but of which we cannot be sure that we shall be ignorant next year. The doctrine is an attempt to found a positive statement upon this ignorance, which can hardly be regarded as justifiable. Spinoza said, "A free man thinks of nothing so little as of death"; it seems to me we may parallel this maxim in the case of thought, and say, "A wise man only remembers his ignorance in order to destroy it." A boundary is that which divides two adjacent portions of space. The question, then, "Has space (in general) a boundary?" involves a contradiction in terms, and is, therefore, unmeaning. But the question, "Does space contain a finite number of cubic miles, or an infinite number?" is a perfectly intelligible and reasonable question which remains to be answered by experiment. The surface of the sea would still contain a finite number of square miles, if there were no land to bound it. Whether or no the space in which we live is of this nature remains to be seen. If its extent is finite, we may quite possibly be able to assign that extent next year; if, on the other hand, it has no end, it is true that the knowledge of that fact would be quite different from any knowledge we at present possess, but we have no right to say that such knowledge is impossible. Either the question will be settled once for all, or the extent of space will be shown to be greater than a quantity which will increase from year to year with the improvement of our sources of knowledge. Either alternative is perfectly conceivable, and there is no contradiction. Observe especially that the supposed contradiction arises from the assumption of theoretical exactness in the laws of geometry. The other case that I mentioned has a very similar origin. The idea of a piece of matter the parts of which are held together by forces, and are capable of being torn asunder by greater forces, is entirely derived from the large pieces of matter which we have to deal with. We do not know whether this idea applies in any sense even to the *molecules* of gases; still less can we apply it to the *atoms* of which they are composed. The word force is used of two phenomena: the pressure, which when two bodies are in contact connects the motion of each with the position of the other; and attraction or repulsion, — that is to say, a change of velocity in one body depending on the position of some other body which is not in contact with it. We do not know that there is anything corresponding to either of these phenomena in the case of a molecule. A meaning can, however, be given to the question of the divisibility of matter in this way. We may ask if there is any piece of matter so small that its properties as matter depend upon its remaining all in one piece. This question is reasonable; but we cannot answer it at present, though we are not at all sure that we shall be equally ignorant next year. If there is no such piece of matter, no such limit to the division which shall leave it matter, the knowledge of that fact would be different from any of our present knowledge; but we have no right to say that it is impossible. If, on the other hand, there *is* a limit, it is quite possible that we may have measured it by the time the Association meets at Bradford. Again, when we are told that the infinite extent of space, for example, is something that we cannot conceive at present, we may reply that this is only natural, since our experience has never yet supplied us with the means of conceiving such things. But then we cannot be sure that the facts will not make us learn to conceive them; in which case they will cease to be inconceivable. In fact, the putting of limits to human conception must always involve the assumption that our previous experience is universally valid in a theoretical sense; an assumption which we have already seen reason to reject. Now you will see that our consideration of this opinion has led us to the true sense of the assertion that the Order of Nature is reasonable. If you will allow me to define a reasonable question as one which is asked in terms of ideas justified by previous experience, without itself contradicting that experience, then we may say, as the result of our investigation, that to every reasonable question there is an intelligible answer which either we or posterity may know.

We have, then, come somehow to the following conclusions. By scientific thought we mean the application of past experience to new circumstances by means of an observed order of events. By saying that this order of events is exact we mean that it is exact enough to correct experiments by, but we do not mean that is theoretically or absolutely exact, because we do not know. The process of inference we found to be in itself an assumption of uniformity, and we found that, as the known exactness of the uniformity became greater, the stringency of the inference increased. By saying that the order of events is reasonable we do not mean that everything has a purpose, or that everything can be explained, or that everything has a cause; for neither of these is true. But we mean that to every reasonable question there is an intelligible answer, which either we or posterity may know *by the exercise of scientific thought.*

For I specially wish you not to go away with the idea that the exercise of scientific thought is properly confined to the subjects from which my illustrations have been chiefly drawn to-night. When the Roman jurists applied their experience of Roman citizens to dealings between citizens and aliens, showing by the difference of their actions that they regarded the circumstances as essentially different, they laid the foundations of that great structure which has guided the social progress of Europe. That procedure was an instance of strictly scientific thought. When a poet finds that he has to move a strange new world which his predecessors have not moved; when, nevertheless, he catches fire from their flashes, arms from their armoury, sustentation from their footprints, the procedure by which he applies old experience to new circumstances is nothing greater or less than scientific thought. When the moralist, studying the conditions of society and the ideas of right and wrong which have come down to us from a time when war was the normal condition of man and success in war the only chance of survival, evolves from them the conditions and ideas which must accompany a time of peace, when the comradeship of equals is the condition of national success; the process by which he does this is scientific thought and nothing else. Remember, then, that it is the guide of action; that the truth which it arrives at is not that which we can ideally contemplate without error, but that which we may act upon without fear; and you cannot fail to see that scientific thought is not an accompaniment or condition of human progress, but human progress itself. And for this reason the question what its characters are, of which I have so inadequately endeavoured to give you some glimpse, is the question of all questions for the human race.

ERWIN SCHRÖDINGER

The Law of Chance

Erwin Schrödinger is one of the founding fathers of twentieth century physics, sharing with W. Heisenberg and P. Dirac the discovery of the modern view of atomic structure, quantum mechanics. It is from this area of physics that the "revolutionary alternative" discussed in the article has grown.

The Problem of Causation in Modern Science

About the middle of the eighteenth century David Hume pointed out that there is no intrinsic connection between cause and effect which can be perceived and understood by the human mind. He further held that the causation of one phenomenon by another (such as the warming of the earth's surface by the rising of the sun) is not directly perceptible. We can only perceive that one phenomenon — the rising of the sun — is always followed by another phenomenon, namely, the warming of the earth's surface. It is also observed that the unfailing succession of certain events after certain others is not confined to any special range of phenomena but is a characteristic feature of Nature. But neither the connection between a single cause and its effect, nor the universality of this connection throughout Nature, is in itself manifest or forms a necessary element in our thought.

The constancy of the laws of nature is guaranteed to us only by experience. Why then do we value this experience for any other reason than that it chronicles past events? Why do we concede to what has happened in the past a controlling influence on our expectation of what is to happen in the future? It is no answer to this question to say that this method of controlling our expectation has proved very useful up to the present, and therefore we cling to it. Such an answer is simply a begging of the question. For that is just the point: why do we expect that what has proved useful hitherto will continue to be so in future? Of course arguments *can* be advanced for adopting this attitude; but this becomes possible only when we change our standpoint. We then perceive that, since the course of events in nature has been governed by regularity up to the present, any species of animals which failed to reap the advantages of allowing their behavior and expectations to be guided by past experience, could not possibly have survived in the struggle for life, but would long ago have been eliminated by so severe a handicap. Hence the mere fact

From *Science Theory and Man* by Erwin Schrödinger. Published by Dover Publications, Inc., New York, N. Y. at $1.35 and reprinted through permission of the publisher. Permission to reprint also given by George Allen and Unwin Ltd., London.

that we, human beings, have survived to raise the question, in a certain sense indicates the required answer!

Hume by no means doubted that in the external world a certain regularity prevails, the observation of which has led us to the very useful and practical concept of a necessary causal connection between one natural occurrence and another. Within the last few years, however, the objective existence of this very regularity has been questioned. The doubts arose from a branch of human study within which we should least expect them — that is to say, the exact science of physics. The basis of this skepticism is the altered viewpoint which we have been compelled to adopt. We have learned to look upon the overwhelming majority of physical and chemical processes as mass phenomena produced by an immensely large number of single individual entities which we call atoms and electrons and molecules. And we have further learned that the extraordinarily precise and exact regularity which we observe in these physical and chemical processes is due to one general law which can be stated thus: In every physical and chemical process there is a transition from relatively well-ordered conditions among the groups of atoms and molecules to less orderly conditions — in other words, a transition from order to disorder, just as might be expected if each individual member of the mass followed its own way more or less without any plan and under no definite law. The exact laws which we observe are "statistical laws." In each mass phenomenon these laws appear all the more clearly, the greater the number of individuals that coöperate in the phenomenon. And the statistical laws are even more clearly manifested when the behavior of each individual entity is *not* strictly determined, but conditioned only by chance. It is quite understandable under such circumstances that a steady transition from regularity to irregularity must result, as a governing Law and as a general basal characteristic of all natural processes. In physics this is believed to be the source from which the very definite one-directional tendency of all natural happenings arises. If an initial state, which may be called the cause, entails a subsequent state, which may be called its effect, the latter, according to the teaching of molecular physics, is always the more haphazard or less orderly one. It is, moreover, precisely the state which can be anticipated with overwhelming probability provided it is admitted that the behavior of the single molecule is absolutely haphazard. And so we have the paradox that, from the point of view of the physicist, chance lies at the root of causality.

I shall now bring forward some examples from every-day life to illustrate how the play of pure chance can result in predictable consequences. Let us take, for instance, a huge library which is visited by thousands of curious people day after day and where all the books are in their regular places on the shelves on the Monday morning when the visitors enter. We shall imagine that these visitors are an unruly pack, badly brought up, and that they have come to sample the books in the library merely out of vulgar curiosity. Let us suppose that whenever they have taken a book from its position on the shelves they never trouble to put it back where it should be placed but replace it quite at random. The general result will be that the library will be submitted to a definite one-directional transition from order to disorder. Now the astonishing feature is that this process proves to be subject to very definite laws, especially if we suppose that the volumes are taken from the shelves in the same haphazard way as they are put back.

Let us investigate the condition of affairs after one week of this barbaric invasion. If we suppose that there were eighty volumes of Goethe's works, for instance, neatly arranged in one section of the library when the casual mob entered, and if we find that only sixty volumes are now in their places while the other twenty are scattered about here and there, then we can expect that during the second week about fifteen volumes will disappear from the row, and about eleven volumes will vanish during the third week, etc. For since we have supposed that the books are taken out quite at random, the probability that one of the remaining volumes will meet with this misfortune decreases as their number decreases. Here we have a general law arising from a mass of chaotic events. The number of volumes in their proper positions diminishes in accordance with the exponential law, or Law of Geometrical Progression, as the mathematicians call it.

We find the very same law verified in many chemical and physical processes, such as the spontaneous transformation of one element into another, in the so-called disintegration of radioactive matter. Now I am sure that in the case of the books in the library the reader will hesitate to admit that the dispersal of Goethe's works would actually follow the predicted law with any appreciable accuracy. And his hesitation is justified. In such a case as this, then, is there any justification whatever for positing any "Law"? Surely the utmost we may legitimately attempt to do is to forecast probabilities. What will actually happen depends on chance. In answer to these objections it must be observed that when we are concerned with only such a small number as eighty volumes of a work in a library, we must indeed be prepared to find that the number actually in place at any given stage will deviate appreciably from the number to be expected according to the "Law." But on the other hand, with 80,000 instead of eighty volumes (in a library containing many millions of books) the casual deviations would amount to only a much smaller fraction of the total number predicted. It is possible to calculate that owing to the myriads of atoms engaged in every physical and chemical process the purely statistical forecasts will be verified with the same degree of exactitude as is actually observed in Nature's laws. But of course they can never hold good with absolute exactitude. Now it is the greatest triumph of the statistical theory of natural law, and the most convincing argument in its favor, that in many cases, such as the radioactive transformation that I have spoken of, small and quite irregular departures from the law really *are* observed. And they have proved to be of just the type and magnitude which the statistical theory had previously calculated.

As a further example of how orderliness springs from chance, we may take the case of insurance companies. The eventualities against which we are insured — accident, death, fire, burglary — depend on a thousand chances. But to the insurance company it makes no difference which of the insured buildings will be burned during the coming year or which of the insured persons will meet with an accident. The only consideration that matters to the company is what percentage of the insured meets with a misfortune that has to be compensated. That percentage can be anticipated from the statistics of former years. Therefore, despite the impossibility of foretelling the fate of any given person, the company may safely undertake, for a relatively small premium, to cover possible damages up to a high multiple of the annual payment.

I have said the statistical theory provides an intelligible explanation of the fact that the course of natural events follows a definite direction, which cannot be reversed. The explanation consists in regarding this unidirectional tendency as a development from a better ordered to a less ordered state (in every single case) of the atomic aggregation involved. We are here concerned with a very general law, the so-called Second Law of Thermodynamics, or the Law of Entropy. We are convinced that this Law governs all physical and chemical processes, even if they result in the most intricate and tangled phenomena, such as organic life, the genesis of a complicated world of organisms from primitive beginnings, the rise and growth of human cultures. In this connection the physicist's belief in a continually increasing disorder seems somewhat paradoxical, and may easily lead to a dreadfully pessimistic misunderstanding of a thesis which actually implies nothing more than the specific meaning assigned to it by the physicist. Therefore a word of explanation will be necessary.

We do not wish to assert anything more than that the *total balance* of disorder in nature is steadily on the increase. In individual sections of the universe, or in definite material systems, the movement may very well be towards a higher degree of order, which is made possible because an adequate compensation occurs in some other systems. Now according to what the physicist calls "order" the heat stored up in the sun represents a fabulous provision for order, insofar as this heat has not yet been distributed equally over the whole universe (though its definite tendency is towards that dispersion), but is for the time being concentrated within a relatively small portion of space. The radiation of heat from the sun, of which a small proportion reaches us, is the compensating process making possible the manifold forms of life and movement on the earth, which frequently present the features of increasing order. A small fraction of the tremendous dissipation suffices to maintain life on the earth by supplying the necessary amount of "order" but of course only so long as the prodigal parent, in its own frantically uneconomic way, is still able to afford the luxury of a planet which is decked out with cloud and wind and rushing rivers and foaming seas and the gorgeous finery of flora and fauna and the striving millions of mankind.

Let us return to the specific question of causality. Here we are still faced with a dilemma. *Either* one can form the opinion that the real essence, or the intrinsic constitution, of the Laws of Nature has been exhaustively discovered through the revelation of their statistical character, and that consequently the idea of a necessary causal connection between natural occurrences ought to be banished from our world picture, just as the concept of heat as a fluid disappeared from physics the moment it was discovered that heat is nothing more than a random movement of the smallest particles. We shall be especially inclined to sacrifice the causal principle if we follow Hume in recognizing that it is not a necessary feature of our thought, but only a convenient habit, generated by the observation of that regularity in the course of actual occurrences the merely statistical character of which is now clearly perceived.

If, however, we disagree with Hume and hold that the causal principle is something of an *a priori* nature, forming a necessary element in our thought, and inevitably marking every possible experience with its stamp, then we must adopt *the second alternative,* which may be expressed as follows: We shall maintain that the behavior of each atom is in every single event determined by rigid causality. And we shall even contend that strictly causal determinism of the elementary processes, although we cannot observe their details, must necessarily be admitted, in order to allow the mass phenomena, which result from their coöperation, to be treated by the methods of statistics and the probability calculus. From this viewpoint causality would lie at the basis of statistical law.

This second view is the conservative one. The former is extremely revolutionary. And the one is the direct antithesis of the other. According to the revolutionary view, undetermined chance is primary and is not further explicable. Law arises only statistically in mass phenomena owing to the coöperation of myriads of chances at play in these phenomena. According to the conservative view the compulsion of law is primary and not further explicable, whereas chance is due to the coöperation of innumerable partial causes which cannot be perceived. Therefore chance here is something subjective — only a name for our own inability to discover the detailed action of numerous small component causes.

There is scarcely any possibility of deciding this issue by experiment. For the methods of pure reasoning evidently allow us either to derive chance from law, or law from chance, whichever we prefer. Wherever we are concerned with a law-determined process forming the ultimate *recognizable* structural element in our world picture, a domain of chance behind it can be supposed to produce the law statistically, if anybody desires to suppose this. And in a similar way the champion of the causal principle is justified in thinking that any chance he observes is dependent on the action of uncontrollable changing causes which give rise to this or that effect, but always compulsorily.

The current controversy about the principle of causality is a phase in our changing intellectual outlook, which is paralleled by the problem of the true character of space and time, a question which has arisen anew as a result of Einstein's theories. The old links between philosophy and physical science, after having been temporarily frayed in many places, are being more closely renewed. The farther physical science progresses the less can it dispense with philosophical criticism. But at the same time philosophers are increasingly obliged to become intimately acquainted with the sphere of research, to which they undertake to prescribe the governing laws of knowledge.

A. M. TURING

Computing Machinery and Intelligence

A. M. Turing's imaginative speculations still influence the development of contemporary digital computers. No one has constructed an "imitation game" as yet, but the "Turing machine" (mentioned only incidentally here) is a widely used concept. Many of the problems raised here are still of active interest.

1. The Imitation Game

I propose to consider the question "Can machines think?" This should begin with definitions of the meaning of the terms "machine" and "think." The definitions might be framed so as to reflect so far as possible the normal use of the words, but this attitude is dangerous. If the meaning of the words "machine" and "think" are to be found by examining how they are commonly used it is difficult to escape the conclusion

A. M. Turing. "Computing Machinery and Intelligence." *Mind*, 59, 433–460, 1950. Reprinted by permission of the editors of *Mind*.

that the meaning and the answer to the question, "Can machines think?" is to be sought in a statistical survey such as a Gallup poll. But this is absurd. Instead of attempting such a definition I shall replace the question by another, which is closely related to it and is expressed in relatively unambiguous words.

The new form of the problem can be described in terms of a game which we call the "imitation game." It is played with three people, a man (A), a woman (B), and an interrogator (C) who may be of either sex. The interrogator stays in a room apart from the other two. The object of the game for the interrogator is to determine which of the other two is the man and which is the woman. He knows them by labels X and Y, and at the end of the game he says either "X is A and Y is B" or "X is B and Y is A." The interrogator is allowed to put questions to A and B thus:

C: Will X please tell me the length of his or her hair?

Now suppose X is actually A, then A must answer. It is A's object in the game to try to cause C to make the wrong identification. His answer might therefore be

"My hair is shingled, and the longest strands are about nine inches long."

In order that tones of voice may not help the interrogator the answers should be written, or better still, typewritten. The ideal arrangement is to have a teleprinter communicating between the two rooms. Alternatively the question and answers can be repeated by an intermediary. The object of the game for the third player (B) is to help the interrogator. The best strategy for her is probably to give truthful answers. She can add such things as "I am the woman, don't listen to him!" to her answers, but it will avail nothing as the man can make similar remarks.

We now ask the question, "What will happen when a machine takes the part of A in this game?" Will the interrogator decide wrongly as often when the game is played like this as he does when the game is played between a man and a woman? These questions replace our original, "Can machines think?"

2. Critique of the New Problem

As well as asking, "What is the answer to this new form of the question," one may ask, "Is this new question a worthy one to investigate?" This latter question we investigate without further ado, thereby cutting short an infinite regress.

The new problem has the advantage of drawing a fairly sharp line between the physical and the intellectual capacities of a man. No engineer or chemist claims to be able to produce a material which is indistinguishable from the human skin. It is possible that at some time this might be done, but even supposing this invention available we should feel there was little point in trying to make a "thinking machine" more human by dressing it up in such artificial flesh. The form in which we have set the problem reflects this fact in the condition which prevents the interrogator from seeing or touching the other competitors, or hearing their voices. Some other advantages of the proposed criterion may be shown up by specimen questions and answers. Thus:

Q: Please write me a sonnet on the subject of the Forth Bridge.
A: Count me out on this one. I never could write poetry.
Q: Add 34957 to 70764.
A: (Pause about 30 seconds and then give as answer) 105621.
Q: Do you play chess?
A: Yes.
Q: I have K at my K1, and no other pieces. You have only K at K6 and R at R1. It is your move. What do you play?
A: (After a pause of 15 seconds) R-R8 mate.

The question and answer method seems to be suitable for introducing almost any one of the fields of human endeavor that we wish to include. We do not wish to penalize the machine for its inability to shine in beauty competitions, nor to penalize a man for losing in a race against an airplane. The conditions of our game make these disabilities irrelevant. The "witnesses" can brag, if they consider it advisable, as much as they please about their charms, strength or heroism, but the interrogator cannot demand practical demonstrations.

The game may perhaps be criticized on the ground that the odds are weighted too heavily against the machine. If the man were to try and pretend to be the machine he would clearly make a very poor showing. He would be given away at once by slowness and inaccuracy in arithmetic. May not machines carry out something which ought to be described as thinking but which is very different from what a man does? This objection is a very strong one, but at least we can say that if, nevertheless, a machine can be constructed to play the imitation game satisfactorily, we need not be troubled by this objection.

It might be urged that when playing the "imitation game" the best strategy for the machine may possibly be something other than imitation of the behavior of a man. This may be, but I think it is unlikely that there is any great effect of this kind. In any case there is no intention to investigate here the theory of the game, and it will be assumed that the best strategy is to try to provide answers that would naturally be given by a man.

3. The Machines Concerned in the Game

The question which we put in §1 will not be quite definite until we have specified what we mean by the word "machine." It is natural that we should wish to permit every kind of engineering technique to be used in our machines. We also wish to allow the possibility that an engineer or team of engineers may construct a machine which works, but whose manner of operation cannot be satisfactorily described by its constructors because they have applied a method which is largely experimental. Finally, we wish to exclude from the machines men born in the usual manner. It is difficult to frame the definitions so as to satisfy these three conditions. One might for instance insist that the team of engineers should be all of one sex, but this would not really be satisfactory, for it is probably possible to rear a complete individual from a single cell of the skin (say) of a man. To do so would be a feat of biological technique deserving of the very highest praise, but we would not be inclined to regard it as a case of "constructing a thinking machine." This prompts us to abandon the requirement that every kind of technique should be permitted. We are the more ready to do so in view of the fact that the present interest in "thinking machines" has been aroused by a particular kind of machine, usually called an "electronic computer" or "digital computer." Following this suggestion we only permit digital computers to take part in our game.

This restriction appears at first sight to be a very drastic one. I shall attempt to show that it is not so in reality. To do this necessitates a short account of the nature and properties of these computers.

It may also be said that this identification of machines with digital computers, like our criterion for "thinking," will only be unsatisfactory if (contrary to my belief), it turns out that digital computers are unable to give a good showing in the game.

There are already a number of digital computers in working order, and it may be asked, "Why not try the experiment straight away? It would be easy to satisfy the conditions of the game. A number of interrogators could be used, and statistics compiled to show how often the right identification was given." The short answer is that we are not asking whether all digital computers would do well in the game nor whether the computers at present available would do well, but whether there are imaginable computers which would do well. But this is only the short answer. We shall see this question in a different light later.

4. Digital Computers

The idea behind digital computers may be explained by saying that these machines are intended to carry out any operations which could be done by a human computer. The human computer is supposed to be following fixed rules; he has no authority to deviate from them in any detail. We may suppose that these rules are supplied in a book, which is altered whenever he is put on to a new job. He has also an unlimited supply of paper on which he does his calculations. He may also do his multiplications and additions on a "desk machine," but this is not important.

If we use the above explanation as a definition we shall be in danger of circularity of argument. We avoid this by giving an outline of the means by which the desired effect is achieved. A digital computer can usually be regarded as consisting of three parts:

(i) Store.
(ii) Executive unit.
(iii) Control.

The store is a store of information, and corresponds to the human computer's paper, whether this is the paper on which he does his calculations or that on which his book of rules is printed. Insofar as the human computer does calculations in his head a part of the store will correpond to his memory.

The executive unit is the part which carries out the various individual operations involved in a calculation. What these individual operations are will vary from machine to machine. Usually fairly lengthy operations can be done such as "Multiply 3540675445 by 7076345687" but in some machines only very simple ones such as "Write down 0" are possible.

We have mentioned that the "book of rules" supplied to the computer is replaced in the machine by a part of the store. It is then called the "table of instructions." It is the duty of the control to see that these instructions are obeyed correctly and in the right order. The control is so constructed that this necessarily happens.

The informations in the store is usually broken up into packets of moderately small size. In one machine, for instance, a packet might consist of ten decimal digits. Numbers are assigned to the parts of the store in which the various packets of information are stored, in some systematic manner. A typical instruction might say —

"Add the number stored in position 6809 to that in 4302 and put the result back into the latter storage position."

Needless to say it would not occur in the machine expressed in English. It would more likely be coded in a form such as 6809430217. Here 17 says which of various possible operations is to be performed on the two numbers. In this case the operation is that described above, viz. "Add the number. . . ." It will be noticed that the instruction takes up 10 digits and so forms one packet of information, very conveniently. The control will normally take the instructions to be obeyed in the order of the positions in which they are stored, but occasionally an instruction such as

"Now obey the instruction stored in position 5606, and continue from there"

may be encountered, or again

"If position 4505 contains 0 obey next the instruction stored in 6707, otherwise continue straight on."

Instructions of these latter types are very important because they make it possible for a sequence of operations to be repeated over and over again until some condition is fulfilled, but in doing so to obey, not fresh instructions on each repetition, but the same ones over and over again. To take a domestic analogy. Suppose Mother wants Tommy to call at the cobbler's every morning on his way to school to see if her shoes are done; she can ask him afresh every morning. Alternatively she can stick up a notice once and for all in the hall which he will see when he leaves for school and which tells him to call for the shoes, and also to destroy the notice when he comes back if he has the shoes with him.

The reader must accept it as a fact that digital computers can be constructed, and indeed have been constructed, according to the principles we have described, and that they can in fact mimic the actions of a human computer very closely.

The book of rules which we have described our human computer as using is of course a convenient fiction. Actual human computers really remember what they have got to do. If one wants to make a machine mimic the behavior of the human computer in some complex operation one has to ask him how it is done, and then translate the answer into the form of an instruction table. Constructing instruction tables is usually described as "programing." To "program a machine to carry out the operation A" means to put the appropriate instruction table into the machine so that it will do A.

An interesting variant on the idea of a digital computer is a "digital computer with a random element." These have instructions involving the throwing of a die or some equivalent electronic process; one such instruction might for instance be, "Throw the die and put the resulting number into store 1000." Sometimes such a machine is described as having free will (though I would not use this phrase myself). It is not normally possible to determine from observing a machine whether it has a random element, for a similar effect can be produced by such devices as making the choices depend on the digits of the decimal for π.

Most actual digital computers have only a finite store. There is no theoretical difficulty in the idea of a computer with an unlimited store. Of course only a finite part can have beeen used at any one time. Likewise only a finite amount can have been constructed, but we can imagine more and more being added as required. Such computers have special theoretical interest and will be called infinite capacity computers.

The idea of a digital computer is an old one. Charles Babbage, Lucasian Professor of Mathematics at Cambridge from 1828 to 1839, planned such a machine, called the Analytical Engine, but it was never completed. Although Babbage had all the essential ideas, his machine was not at that time such a very attractive prospect. The speed which would have been available would be definitely faster than a human computer but something like 100 times slower than the Manchester machine, itself one of the slower of the modern machines. The storage was to be purely mechanical, using wheels and cards.

The fact that Babbage's Analytical Engine was to be entirely mechanical will help us to rid ourselves of a superstition. Importance is often attached to the fact that modern digital computers are electrical, and that the nervous system also is electrical. Since Babbage's machine was not electrical, and since all digital computers are in a sense equivalent, we see that this use of electricity cannot be of theoretical importance. Of course electricity usually comes in where fast signaling is concerned, so that it is not surprising that we find it in both these connections. In the nervous system chemical phenomena are at least as important as electrical. In certain computers the storage system is mainly acoustic. The feature of using electricity is thus seen to be only a very superficial similarity. If we wish to find such similarities we should look rather for mathematical analogies of function.

5. Universality of Digital Computers

The digital computers considered in the last section may be classified among the "discrete state machines." These are the machines which move by sudden jumps or clicks from one quite definite state to another. These states are sufficiently different for the possibility of confusion between them to be ignored. Strictly speaking there are no such machines. Everything really moves continuously. But there are many kinds of machines which can profitably be *thought of* as being discrete state machines. For instance in considering the switches for a lighting system it is a convenient fiction that each switch must be definitely on or definitely off. There must be intermediate positions, but for most purposes we can forget about them. As an example of a discrete state machine we might consider a wheel which clicks round through 120° once a second, but may be stopped by a lever which can be operated from outside; in addition a lamp is to light in one of the positions of the wheel. This machine could be described abstractly as follows: The internal state of the machine (which is described by the position of the wheel) may be q_1, q_2 or q_3. There is an input signal i_0 or i_1 (position of lever). The internal state at any moment is determined by the last state and input signal according to the table

		Last State		
		q_1	q_2	q_3
Input	i_0	q_2	q_3	q_1
	i_1	q_1	q_2	q_3

The output signals, the only externally visible indication of the internal state (the light) are described by the table

State	q_1	q_2	q_3
Output	o_0	o_0	o_1

This example is typical of discrete state machines. They can be described by such tables provided they have only a finite number of possible states.

It will seem that given the initial state of the machine and the input signals it is always possible to predict all future states. This is reminiscent of Laplace's view that from the complete state of the universe at one moment of time, as described by the positions and velocities of all particles, it should be possible to predict all future states. The prediction which we are considering is, however, rather nearer to practicability than that considered by Laplace. The system of the "universe as a whole" is such that quite small errors in the initial conditions can have an overwhelming effect at a later time. The displacement of a single electron by a billionth of a centimeter at one moment might make the difference betweeen a man being killed by an avalanche a year later, or escaping. It is an essential property of the mechanical systems which we have called "discrete state machines" that this phenomenon does not occur. Even when we consider the actual physical machines instead of the idealized machines, reasonably accurate knowledge of the state at one moment yields reasonably accurate knowledge any number of steps later.

As we have mentioned, digital computers fall within the class of discrete state machines. But the number of states of which such a machine is capable is usually enormously large. For instance, the number for the machine now working at Manchester is about $2^{165,000}$, i.e., about $10^{50,000}$. Compare this with our example of the clicking wheel described above, which had three states. It is not difficult to see why the number of states should be so immense. The computer includes a store corresponding to the paper used by a human computer. It must be possible to write into the store any one of the combinations of symbols which might have been written on the paper. For simplicity suppose that only digits from 0 to 9 are used as symbols. Variations in handwriting are ignored. Suppose the computer is allowed 100 sheets of paper each containing 50 lines each with room for 30 digits. Then the number of states is $10^{100 \times 50 \times 30}$, i.e., $10^{150,000}$. This is about the number of states of three Manchester machines put together. The logarithm to the base two of the number of states is usually called the "storage capacity" of the machine. Thus the Manchester machine has a storage capacity of about 165,000 and the wheel machine of our example about $1 \cdot 6$. If two machines are put together their capacities must be added to obtain the capacity of the resultant machine. This leads to the possibility of statements such as "The Manchester machine contains 64 magnetic tracks each with a capacity of 2560, eight electronic tubes with a capacity of 1280. Miscellaneous storage amounts to about 300 making a total of 174,380."

Given the table corresponding to a discrete state machine it is possible to predict what it will do. There is no reason why this calculation should not be carried out by means of a digital computer. Provided it could be carried out sufficiently quickly the digital computer could mimic the behavior of any discrete state machine. The imitation game could then be played with the machine in question (as B) and the mimicking digital computer (as A) and the interrogator would be unable to distinguish them. Of course the digital computer must have an adequate storage capacity as well as working sufficiently fast. Moreover, it must be programed afresh for each new machine which it is desired to mimic.

This special property of digital computers, that they can mimic any discrete state machine, is described by saying that they are *universal* machines. The existence of machines with this property has the important consequence that, considerations of speed apart, it is unnecessary to design various new machines to do various computing processes. They can all be done with one digital computer, suitably programed for each case. It will be seen that as a consequence of this all digital computers are in a sense equivalent.

We may now consider again the point raised at the end of §3. It was suggested tentatively that the question, "Can machines think?" should be replaced by "Are there imaginable digital computers which would do well in the imitation game?" If we wish we can make this superficially more general and ask "Are there discrete state machines which would do well?" But in view of the universality property we see that either of these questions is equivalent to this, "Let us fix our attention on one particular digital computer C. Is it true that by modifying this computer to have an adequate storage, suitably increasing its speed of action, and providing it with an appropriate program, C can be made to play satisfactorily the part of A in the imitation game, the part of B being taken by a man?"

6. Contrary Views on the Main Question

We may now consider the ground to have been cleared and we are ready to proceed to the debate on our question, "Can machines think?" and the variant of it quoted at the end of the last section. We cannot altogether abandon the original form of the problem, for opinions will differ as to the appropriateness of the substitution and we must at least listen to what has to be said in this connection.

It will simplify matters for the reader if I explain first my own beliefs in the matter. Consider first the more accurate form of the question. I believe that in about fifty years' time it will be possible to program computers, with a storage capacity of about 10^9, to make them play the imitation game so well that an average interrogator will not have more than 70 per cent chance of making the right identification after five minutes of questioning. The original question, "Can machines think?" I believe to be too meaningless to deserve discussion. Nevertheless I believe that at the end of the century the use of words and general educated opinion will have altered so much that one will be able to speak of machines thinking without expecting to be contradicted. I believe further that no useful purpose is served by concealing these beliefs. The popular view that scientists proceed inexorably from well-established fact to well-established fact, never being influenced by any unproved conjecture, is quite mistaken. Provided it is made clear which are proved facts and which are conjectures, no harm can result. Conjectures are of great importance since they suggest useful lines of research.

I now proceed to consider opinions opposed to my own

(1) *The Theological Objection.* Thinking is a function of man's immortal soul. God has given an immortal soul to every man and woman, but not to any other animal or to machines. Hence no animal or machine can think.[1]

I am unable to accept any part of this, but will attempt to reply in theological terms. I should find the argument more convincing if animals were classed with men, for there is a greater difference, to my mind, between the typical animate and the inanimate than there is between man and the other animals. The arbitrary character of the orthodox view becomes clearer if we consider how it might appear to a member of some other religious community. How do Christians regard the Moslem view

---

[1] Possibly this view is heretical. St. Thomas Aquinas [*Summa Theologica,* quoted by Bertrand Russell, *A History of Western Philosophy* (New York: Simon and Schuster, 1945), p. 458] states that God cannot make a man to have no soul. But this may not be a real restriction on His powers, but only a result of the fact that men's souls are immortal, and therefore indestructible.

that women have no souls? But let us leave this point aside and return to the main argument. It appears to me that the argument quoted above implies a serious restriction of the omnipotence of the Almighty. It is admitted that there are certain things that He cannot do such as making one equal to two, but should we not believe that He has freedom to confer a soul on an elephant if He sees fit? We might expect that He would only exercise this power in conjunction with a mutation which provided the elephant with an appropriately improved brain to minister to the needs of this soul. An argument of exactly similar form may be made for the case of machines. It may seem different because it is more difficult to "swallow." But this really only means that we think it would be less likely that He would consider the circumstances suitable for conferring a soul. The circumstances in question are discussed in the rest of this paper. In attempting to construct such machines we should not be irreverently usurping His power of creating souls, any more than we are in the pro-creation of children: rather we are, in either case, instruments of His will providing mansions for the souls that He creates.

However, this is mere speculation. I am not very impressed with theological arguments whatever they may be used to support. Such arguments have often been found unsatisfactory in the past. In the time of Galileo it was argued that the texts, "And the sun stood still . . . and hasted not to go down about a whole day" (Joshua x. 13) and "He laid the foundations of the earth, that it should not move at any time" (Psalm cv. 5) were an adequate refutation of the Copernican theory. With our present knowledge such an argument appears futile. When that knowledge was not available it made a quite different impression.

(2) *The "Heads in the Sand" Objection.* "The consequences of machines thinking would be too dreadful. Let us hope and believe that they cannot do so."

This argument is seldom expressed quite so openly as in the form above. But it affects most of us who think about it at all. We like to believe that Man is in some subtle way superior to the rest of creation. It is best if he can be shown to be *necessarily* superior, for then there is no danger of him losing his commanding position. The popularity of the theological argument is clearly connected with this feeling. It is likely to be quite strong in intellectual people, since they value the power or thinking more highly than others, and are more inclined to base their belief in the superiority of Man on this power.

I do not think that this argument is sufficiently substantial to require refutation. Consolation would be more appropriate: perhaps this should be sought in the transmigration of souls.

(3) *The Mathematical Objection.* There are a number of results of mathematical logic which can be used to show that there are limitations

to the powers of discrete state machines. The best known of these results is known as Gödel's theorem, and shows that in any sufficiently powerful logical system statements can be formulated which can neither be proved nor disproved within the system, unless possibly the system itself is inconsistent. There are other, in some respects similar, results due to Church, Kleene, Rosser, and Turing. The latter result is the most convenient to consider, since it refers directly to machines, whereas the others can only be used in a comparatively indirect argument: for instance if Gödel's theorem is to be used we need in addition to have some means of describing logical systems in terms of machines, and machines in terms of logical systems. The result in question refers to a type of machine which is essentialy a digital computer with an infinite capacity. It states that there are certain things that such a machine cannot do. If it is rigged up to give answers to questions as in the imitation game, there will be some questions to which it will either give a wrong answer, or fail to give an answer at all however much time is allowed for a reply. There may, of course, be many such questions, and questions which cannot be answered by one machine may be satisfactorily answered by another. We are of course supposing for the present that the questions are of the kind to which an answer "Yes" or "No" is appropriate, rather than questions such as "What do you think of Picasso?" The questions that we know the machines must fail on are of this type, "Consider the machine specified as follows. . . . Will this machine ever answer 'Yes' to any question?" The dots are to be replaced by a description of some machine in a standard form, which could be something like that used in Sec. 5. When the machine described bears a certain comparatively simple relation to the machine which is under interrogation, it can be shown that the answer is either wrong or not forthcoming. This is the mathematical result: it is argued that it proves a disability of machines to which the human intellect is not subject.

The short answer to this argument is that although it is established that there are limitations to the powers of any particular machine, it has only been stated, without any sort of proof, that no such limitations apply to the human intellect. But I do not think this view can be dismissed quite so lightly. Whenever one of these machines is asked the appropriate critical question, and gives a definite answer, we know that this answer must be wrong, and this gives us a certain feeling of superiority. Is this feeling illusory? It is no doubt quite genuine, but I do not think too much importance should be attached to it. We too often give wrong answers to questions ourselves to be justified in being very pleased at such evidence of fallibility on the part of the machines. Further, our superiority can only be felt on such an occasion in relation to the one machine over which we have scored our petty triumph. There would be no question of triumphing simultaneously over *all* machines. In short, then, there might be men cleverer than any given machine, but then again there might be other machines cleverer again, and so on.

Those who hold to the mathematical argument would, I think, mostly be willing to accept the imitation game as a basis for discussion. Those who believe in the two previous objections would probably not be interested in any criteria.

(4) *The Argument from Consciousness*. This argument is very well expressed in Professor Jefferson's Lister Oration for 1949, from which I quote. "Not until a machine can write a sonnet or compose a concerto because of thoughts and emotions felt, and not by the chance fall of symbols, could we agree that machine equals brain—that is, not only write it but know that it had written it. No mechanism could feel (and not merely artificially signal, an easy contrivance) pleasure at its successes, grief when its valves fuse, be warmed by flattery, be made miserable by its mistakes, be charmed by sex, be angry or depressed when it cannot get what it wants."

This argument appears to be a denial of the validity of our test. According to the most extreme form of this view the only way by which one could be sure that a machine thinks is to *be* the machine and to feel oneself thinking. One could then describe these feelings to the world, but of course no one would be justified in taking any notice. Likewise according to this view the only way to know that a *man* thinks is to be that particular man. It is in fact the solipsist point of view. It may be the most logical view to hold but it makes communication of ideas difficult. A is liable to believe "A thinks but B does not" while B believes "B thinks but A does not." Instead of arguing continually over this point it is usual to have the polite convention that everyone thinks.

I am sure that Professor Jefferson does not wish to adopt the extreme and solipsist point of view. Probably he would be quite willing to accept the imitation game as a test. The game (with the player B omitted) is frequently used in practice under the name of *viva voce* to discover whether someone really understands something or has "learned it parrot fashion." Let us listen in to a part of such a *viva voce*:

Interrogator: In the first line of your sonnet which reads "Shall I compare thee to a summer's day," would not "a spring day" do as well or better?

Witness: It wouldn't scan.

Interrogator: How about "a winter's day." That would scan all right.

Witness: Yes, but nobody wants to be compared to a winter's day.

Interrogator: Would you say Mr. Pickwick reminded you of Christmas?

Witness: In a way.

Interrogator: Yet Christmas is a winter's day, and I do not think Mr.
Pickwick would mind the comparison.

Witness: I don't think you're serious. By a winter's day one means a
typical winter's day, rather than a special one like Christmas.

And so on. What would Professor Jefferson say if the sonnet-writing
machine was able to answer like this in the *viva voce?* I do not know
whether he would regard the machine as "merely artificially signaling"
these answers, but if the answers were as satisfactory and sustained as in
the above passage I do not think he would describe it as "an easy contrivance." This phrase is, I think, intended to cover such devices as the
inclusion in the machine of a record of someone reading a sonnet, with
appropriate switching to turn it on from time to time.

In short then, I think that most of those who support the argument
from consciousness could be persuaded to abandon it rather than be
forced into the solipsist position. They will then probably be willing to
accept our test.

I do not wish to give the impression that I think there is no mystery
about consciousness. There is, for instance, something of a paradox connected with any attempt to localize it. But I do not think these mysteries
necessarily need to be solved before we can answer the question with
which we are concerned in this paper.

(5) *Arguments from Various Disabilities.* These arguments take the
form, "I grant you that you can make machines do all the things you have
mentioned but you will never be able to make one to do X." Numerous
features X are suggested in this connection. I offer a selection:

> "Be kind, resourceful, beautiful, friendly (p. 19), have initiative, have a
> sense of humor, tell right from wrong, make mistakes (p. 19), fall in love,
> enjoy strawberries and cream (p. 19), make someone fall in love with it,
> learn from experience (pp. 25f.), use words properly, be the subject of its
> own thought (p. 20), have as much diversity of behavior as a man, do
> something really new (p. 20). (Some of these disabilities are given special
> consideration as indicated by the page numbers.)"

No support is usually offered for these statements. I believe they are
mostly founded on the principle of scientific induction. A man has seen
thousands of machines in his lifetime. From what he sees of them he
draws a number of general conclusions. They are ugly, each is designed
for a very limited purpose, when required for a minutely different purpose
they are useless, the variety of behavior of any one of them is very small,
etc., etc. Naturally he concludes that these are necessary properties of
machines in general. Many of these limitations are associated with the
very small storage capacity of most machines. (I am assuming that the
idea of storage capacity is extended in some way to cover machines other
than discrete state machines. The exact definition does not matter as

no mathematical accuracy is claimed in the present discussion.) A few years ago, when very little had been heard of digital computers, it was possible to elicit much incredulity concerning them, if one mentioned their properties without describing their construction. That was presumably due to a similar application of the principle of scientific induction. These applications of the principle are of course largely unconscious. When a burned child fears the fire and shows that he fears it by avoiding it, I should say that he was applying scientific induction. (I could of course also describe his behavior in many other ways.) The works and customs of mankind do not seem to be very suitable material to which to apply scientific induction. A very large part of space-time must be investigated if reliable results are to be obtained. Otherwise we may (as most English children do) decide that everybody speaks English, and that it is silly to learn French.

There are, however, special remarks to be made about many of the disabilities that have been mentioned. The inability to enjoy strawberries and cream may have struck the reader as frivolous. Possibly a machine might be made to enjoy this delicious dish, but any attempt to make one do so would be idiotic. What is important about this disability is that it contributes to some of the other disabilities, e.g., to the difficulty of the same kind of friendliness occurring between man and machine as between white man and white man, or between black man and black man.

The claim that "machines cannot make mistakes" seems a curious one. One is tempted to retort, "Are they any the worse for that?" But let us adopt a more sympathetic attitude, and try to see what is really meant. I think this criticism can be explained in terms of the imitation game. It is claimed that the interrogator could distinguish the machine from the man simply by setting them a number of problems in arithmetic. The machine would be unmasked because of its deadly accuracy. The reply to this is simple. The machine (programed for playing the game) would not attempt to give the *right* answers to the arithmetic problems. It would deliberately introduce mistakes in a manner calculated to confuse the interrogator. A mechanical fault would probably show itself through an unsuitable decision as to what sort of a mistake to make in the arithmetic. Even this interpretation of the criticism is not sufficiently sympathetic. But we cannot afford the space to go into it much further. It seems to me that this criticism depends on a confusion between two kinds of mistakes. We may call them "errors of functioning" and "errors of conclusion." Errors of functioning are due to some mechanical or electrical fault which causes the machine to behave otherwise than it was designed to do. In philosophical discussions one likes to ignore the possibility of such errors; one is therefore discussing "abstract machines." These abstract machines are mathematical fictions rather than physical objects.

By definition they are incapable of errors of functioning. In this sense we can truly say that "machines can never make mistakes." Errors of conclusion can only arise when some meaning is attached to the output signals from the machine. The machine might, for instance, type out mathematical equations, or sentences in English. When a false proposition is typed we say that the machine has committed an error of conclusion. There is clearly no reason at all for saying that a machine cannot make this kind of mistake. It might do nothing but type out repeatedly "$0 = 1$." To take a less perverse example, it might have some method for drawing conclusions by scientific induction. We must expect such a method to lead occasionally to erroneous results.

The claim that a machine cannot be the subject of its own thought can of course only be answered if it can be shown that the machine has *some* thought with *some* subject matter. Nevertheless, "the subject matter of a machine's operations" does seem to mean something, at least to the people who deal with it. If, for instance, the machine was trying to find a solution of the equation $x^2 - 40x - 11 = 0$ one would be tempted to describe this equation as part of the machine's subject matter at that moment. In this sort of sense a machine undoubtedly can be its own subject matter. It may be used to help in making up its own programs, or to predict the effect of alterations in its own structure. By observing the results of its own behavior it can modify its own programs so as to achieve some purpose more effectively. These are possibilities of the near future, rather than Utopian dreams.

The criticism that a machine cannot have much diversity of behavior is just a way of saying that it cannot have much storage capacity. Until fairly recently a storage capacity of even a thousand digits was very rare.

The criticisms that we are considering here are often disguised forms of the argument from consciousness. Usually if one maintains that a machine *can* do one of these things, and describes the kind of method that the machine could use, one will not make much of an impression. It is thought that the method (whatever it may be, for it must be mechanical) is really rather base. Compare the parenthesis in Jefferson's statement quoted above.

(6) *Lady Lovelace's Objection.* Our most detailed information of Babbage's Analytical Engine comes from a memoir by Lady Lovelace. In it she states, "The analytical Engine has no pretensions to *originate* anything. It can do *whatever we know how to order it* to perform" (her italics). This statement is quoted by Hartree who adds: "This does not imply that it may not be possible to construct electronic equipment which will 'think for itself,' or in which, in biological terms, one could set up a conditioned reflex, which would serve as a basis for 'learning.' Whether this is possible in principle or not is a stimulating and exciting

question, suggested by some of these recent developments. But it did not seem that the machines constructed or projected at the time had this property."

I am in thorough agreement with Hartree over this. It will be noticed that he does not assert that the machines in question had not got the property, but rather that the evidence available to Lady Lovelace did not encourage her to believe that they had it. It is quite possible that the machines in question had in a sense got this property. For suppose that some discrete state machine has the property. The Analytical Engine was a universal digital computer, so that, if its storage capacity and speed were adequate, it could by suitable programing be made to mimic the machine in question. Probably this argument did not occur to the Countess or to Babbage. In any case there was no obligation on them to claim all that could be claimed.

This whole question will be considered again under the heading of learning machines.

A variant of Lady Lovelace's objection states that a machine can "never do anything really new." This may be parried for a moment with the saw, "There is nothing new under the sun." Who can be certain that "original work" that he has done was not simply the growth of the seed planted in him by teaching, or the effect of following well-known general principles. A better variant of the objection says that a machine can never "take us by surprise." This statement is a more direct challenge and can be met directly. Machines take me by surprise with great frequency. This is largely because I do not do sufficient calculation to decide what to expect them to do, or rather because, although I do a calculation, I do it in a hurried, slipshod fashion, taking risks. Perhaps I say to myself, "I suppose the voltage here ought to be the same as there: anyway let's assume it is." Naturally I am often wrong, and the result is a surprise for me, for by the time the experiment is done these assumptions have been forgotten. These admissions lay me open to lectures on the subject of my vicious ways, but do not throw any doubt on my credibility when I testify to the surprises I experience.

I do not expect this reply to silence my critic. He will probably say that such surprises are due to some creative mental act on my part, and reflect no credit on the machine. This leads us back to the argument from consciousness, and far from the idea of surprise. It is a line of argument we must consider closed, but it is perhaps worth remarking that the appreciation of something as surprising requires as much of a "creative mental act" whether the surprising event originates from a man, a book, a machine or anything else.

The view that machines cannot give rise to surprises is due, I believe, to a falacy to which philosophers and mathematicians are particularly subject. This is the assumption that as soon as a fact is presented to a mind all consequences of that fact spring into the mind. simultaneously with it. It is a very useful assumption under many circumstances, but one too easily forgets that it is false. A natural consequence of doing so is that one then assumes that there is no virtue in the mere working out of consequences from data and general principles.

(7) *Argument from Continuity in the Nervous System.* The nervous system is certainly not a discrete state machine. A small error in the information about the size of a nervous impulse impinging on a neuron, may make a large difference to the size of the outgoing impulse. It may be argued that, this being so, one cannot expect to be able to mimic the behavior of the nervous system with a discrete state system.

It is true that a discrete state machine must be different from a continuous machine. But if we adhere to the conditions of the imitation game, the interrogator will not be able to take any advantage of this difference. The situation can be made clearer if we consider some other simpler continuous machine. A differential analyzer will do very well. (A differential analyzer is a certain kind of machine not of the discrete state type used for some kinds of calculation.) Some of these provide their answers in a typed form, and so are suitable for taking part in the game. It would not be possible for a digital computer to predict exactly what answers the differential analyzer would give to a problem, but it would be quite capable of giving the right sort of answer. For instance, if asked to give the value of π (actually about $3 \cdot 1416$) it would be resonable to choose at random between the values $3 \cdot 12$, $3 \cdot 13$, $3 \cdot 14$, $3 \cdot 15$, $3 \cdot 16$ with the probabilities of $0 \cdot 05$, $0 \cdot 15$, $0 \cdot 55$, $0 \cdot 19$, $0 \cdot 06$ (say). Under these circumstances it would be very difficult for the interrogator to distinguish the differential analyzer from the digital computer.

(8) *The Argument from Informality of Behavior.* It is not possible to produce a set of rules purporting to describe what a man should do in every conceivable set of circumstances. One might for instance have a rule that one is to stop when one sees a red traffic light, and to go if one sees a green one, but what if by some fault both appear together? One may perhaps decide that it is safest to stop. But some further difficulty may well arise from this decision later. To attempt to provide rules of conduct to cover every eventuality, even those arising from traffic lights, appears to be impossible. With all this I agree.

From this it is argued that we cannot be machines. I shall try to reproduce the argument, but I fear I shall hardly do it justice. It seems to run something like this. "If each man had a definite set of rules of conduct by which he regulated his life he would be no better than a machine. But there are no such rules, so men cannot be machines." The undistributed middle is glaring. I do not think the argument is ever put quite like this, but I believe this is the argument used nevertheless. There may however be a certain confusion between "rules of conduct" and "laws of behavior" to cloud the issue. By "rules of conduct" I mean precepts such as "Stop if you see red lights," on which one can act, and of which one can be conscious. By "laws of behavior" I mean laws of nature as applied to a man's body such as "if you pinch him he will squeak." If we substitute "laws of behavior which regulate his life" for "laws of conduct by which he regulates his life" in the argument quoted the undistributed middle is no longer insuperable. For we believe that it is not only true that being regulated by laws of behavior implies being some sort of machine (though not necessarily a discrete state machine), but that conversely being such a machine implies being regulated by such laws. However, we cannot so easily convince ourselves of the absence of complete laws of behavior as of complete rules of conduct. The only way we know of for finding such laws is scientific observation, and we certainly know of no circumstances under which we could say, "We have searched enough. There are no such laws."

We can demonstrate more forcibly that any such statement would be unjustified. For suppose we could be sure of finding such laws if they existed. Then given a discrete state machine it should certainly be possible to discover by observation sufficient about it to predict its future behavior, and this within a reasonable time, say a thousand years. But this does not seem to be the case. I have set up on the Manchester computer a small program using only 1000 units of storage, whereby the machine supplied with one sixteen figure number replies with another within two seconds. I would defy anyone to learn from these replies sufficient about the program to be able to predict any replies to untried values.

(9) *The Argument from Extra-Sensory Perception.* I assume that the reader is familiar with the idea of extra-sensory perception, and the meaning of the four items of it, viz., telepathy, clairvoyance, precognition and psychokinesis. These disturbing phenomena seem to deny all our usual scientific ideas. How we should like to discredit them! Unfortunately the statistical evidence, at least for telepathy, is overwhelming. It is very difficult to rearrange one's ideas so as to fit these new facts in. Once one has accepted them it does not seem a very big step to believe in ghosts and bogies. The idea that our bodies move simply according to the known laws of physics, together with some others not yet discovered but somewhat similar, would be one of the first to go.

This argument is to my mind quite a strong one. One can say in reply that many scientific theories seem to remain workable in practice, in spite of clashing with E.S.P.; that in fact one can get along very nicely if one forgets about it. This is rather cold comfort, and one fears that thinking is just the kind of phenomenon where E.S.P. may be especially relevant.

A more specific argument based on E.S.P. might run as follows: "Let us play the imitation game, using as witnesses a man who is good as a telepathic receiver, and a digital computer. The interrogator can ask such questions as 'What suit does the card in my right hand belong to?' The man by telepathy or clairvoyance gives the right answer 130 times out of 400 cards. The machine can only guess at random, and perhaps get 104 right, so the interrogator makes the right identification." There is an interesting possibility which opens here. Suppose the digital computer contains a random number generator. Then it will be natural to use this to decide what answer to give. But then the random number generator will be subject to the psychokinetic powers of the interrogator. Perhaps this psychokinesis might cause the machine to guess right more often than would be expected on a probability calculation, so that the interrogator might still be unable to make the right identification On the other hand, he might be able to guess right without any questioning, by clairvoyance. With E.S.P. anything may happen.

If telepathy is admitted it will be necessary to tighten our test. The situation could be regarded as analogous to that which would occur if the interrogator were talking to himself and one of the competitors was listening with his ear to the wall. To put the competitors into a "telepathy-proof room" would satisfy all requirements.

7. Learning Machines

The reader will have anticipated that I have no very convincing arguments of a positive nature to support my views. If I had I should not have taken such pains to point out the fallacies in contrary views. Such evidence as I have I shall now give.

Let us return for a moment to Lady Lovelace's objection, which stated that the machine can only do what we tell it to do. One could say that a man can "inject" an idea into the machine, and that it will respond to a certain extent and then drop into quiescence, like a piano string struck by a hammer. Another simile would be an atomic pile of less than critical size: an injected idea is to correspond to a neutron entering the pile from without. Each such neutron will cause a certain disturbance which eventually dies away. If, however, the size of the pile is sufficiently increased, the disturbance caused by such an incoming neutron will very likely go on and on increasing until the whole pile is destroyed. Is there a corresponding phenomenon for minds, and is there one for machines? There does seem to be one for the human mind. The majority of them seem to be "subcritical," i.e., to correspond in this analogy to piles of subcritical size. An idea presented to such a mind will on an average give rise to less than one idea in reply. A smallish proportion are supercritical. An idea presented to such a mind may give rise to a whole "theory" consisting of secondary, tertiary and more remote ideas. Animals' minds seem to be very definitely subcritical. Adhering to this analogy we ask, "Can a machine be made to be supercritical?"

The "skin of an onion" analogy is also helpful. In considering the functions of the mind or the brain we find certain operations which we can explain in purely mechanical terms. This we say does not correspond to the real mind: it is a sort of skin which we must strip off if we are to find the real mind. But then in what remains we find a further skin to be stripped off, and so on. Proceeding in this way do we ever come to the "real" mind, or do we eventually come to the skin which has nothing in it? In the latter case the whole mind is mechanical. (It would not be a discrete state machine however. We have discussed this.)

These last two paragraphs do not claim to be convincing arguments. They should rather be described as "recitations tending to produce belief."

The only really satisfactory support that can be given for the view expressed at the beginning of Sec. 6 will be that provided by waiting for the end of the century and then doing the experiment described. But what can we say in the meantime? What steps should be taken now if the experiment is to be successful?

As I have explained, the problem is mainly one of programing. Advances in engineering will have to be made too, but it seems unlikely that these will not be adequate for the requirements. Estimates of the storage capacity of the brain vary from 10^{10} to 10^{15} binary digits. I incline to the lower values and believe that only a very small fraction is used for the higher types of thinking. Most of it is probably used for the retention of visual impressions. I should be surprised if more than 10^9 was required for satisfactory playing of the imitation game, at any rate against a blind man. (Note: The capacity of the *Encyclopaedia Britannica,* eleventh edition, is 2×10^9.) A storage capacity of 10^7 would be a very practicable possibility even by present techniques. It is probably not necessary to increase the speed of operations of the machines at all. Parts of modern machines which can be regarded as analogues of nerve cells work about a thousand times faster than the latter. This should provide a "margin of safety" which could cover losses of speed arising in many ways. Our problem then is to find out how to program these machines to play the game. At my present rate of working I produce about a thousand digits of program a day, so that about sixty workers, working steadily through the fifty years might accomplish the job, if nothing went into the wastepaper basket. Some more expeditious method seems desirable.

In the process of trying to imitate an adult human mind we are bound to think a good deal about the process which has brought it to the state that it is in. We may notice three components,

(*a*) The initial state of the mind, say at birth,

(*b*) The education to which it has been subjected,

(*c*) Other experience, not to be described as education, to which it has been subjected.

Instead of trying to produce a program to simulate the adult mind, why not rather try to produce one which simulates the child's? If this were then subjected to an appropriate course of education one would obtain the adult brain. Presumably the child-brain is something like a notebook as one buys it from the stationers. Rather little mechanism, and lots of blank sheets. (Mechanism and writing are from our point of view almost synonymous.) Our hope is that there is so little mechanism in the child-grain that something like it can be easily programed. The amount of work in the education we can assume, as a first approximation, to be much the same as for the human child.

We have thus divided our problem into two parts — The child-program and the education process. These two remain very closely connected. We cannot expect to find a good child-machine at the first attempt. One must experiment with teaching one such machine and see how well it learns. One can then try another and see if it is better or worse. There is an obvious connection between this process and evolution, by the identifications

Structure of the child-machine = Hereditary material
Changes   "   "   "   "   = Mutations
Natural selection   = Judgment of the experimenter

One may hope, however, that this process will be more expeditious than evolution. The survival of the fittest is a slow method for measuring advantages. The experimenter, by the exercise of intelligence, should be able to speed it up. Equally important is the fact that he is not restricted to random mutations. If he can trace a cause for some weakness he can probably think of the kind of mutation which will improve it.

It will not be possible to apply exactly the same teaching process to the machine as to a normal child. It will not, for instance, be provided with legs, so that it could not be asked to go out and fill the coal scuttle. Possibly it might not have eyes. But however well these deficiencies might be overcome by clever engineering, one could not send the creature to school without the other children making excessive fun of it. It must be given some tuition. We need not be too concerned about the legs, eyes, etc. The example of Miss Helen Keller shows that education can take place provided that communication in both directions between teacher and pupil can take place by some means or other.

We normally associate punishments and rewards with the teaching process. Some simple child-machines can be constructed or programed on this sort of principle. The machine has to be so constructed that events which shortly preceded the occurrence of a punishment-signal are unlikely to be repeated, whereas a reward-signal increases the probability of repetition of the events which led up to it. These definitions do not presuppose any feelings on the part of the machine. I have done some experiments with one such child-machine, and succeeded in teaching it a few things, but the teaching method was too unorthodox for the experiment to be considered really successful.

The use of punishments and rewards can at best be a part of the teaching process. Roughly speaking, if the teacher has no other means of communicating to the pupil, the amount of information which can reach him does not exceed the total number of rewards and punishments applied. By the time a child has learned to repeat "Casabianca" he would probably feel very sore indeed, if the text could only be discovered by a "Twenty Questions" technique, every "NO" taking the form of a blow. It is necessary therefore to have some other "unemotional" channels of communication. If these are available it is possible to teach a machine by punishments and rewards to obey orders given in some language, e.g., a symbolic language. These orders are to be transmitted through the "unemotional" channels. The use of this language will diminish greatly the number of punishments and rewards required.

Opinions may vary as to the complexity which is suitable in the child-machine. One might try to make it as simple as possible consistently with the general principles. Alternatively one might have a complete system of logical inference "built in."[2] In the latter case the store would be largely occupied with definitions and propositions. The propositions would have various kinds of status, e.g., well-established facts, conjectures, mathematically proved therems, statements given by an authority, expressions having the logical form of proposition but not belief-value. Certain propositions may be described as "imperatives." The machine should be so constructed that as soon as an imperative is classed as "well-established" the appropriate action automatically takes place. To illustrate this, suppose the teacher says to the machine, "Do your homework now." This may cause "Teacher says 'Do your homework now'" to be included among the well-established facts. Another such fact might be, "Everything that teacher says is true." Combining these may eventually lead to the imperative, "Do your homework now," being included among the well-established facts, and this, by the construction of the machine, will mean that the homework actually gets started, but the effect is very unsatisfac-

[2] Or rather "programed in" for our child-machine will be programed in a digital computer. But the logical system will not have to be learned.

tory. The processes of inference used by the machine need not be such as would satisfy the most exacting logicians. There might for instance be no hierarchy of types. But this need not mean that type fallacies will occur, any more than we are bound to fall over unfenced cliffs. Suitable imperatives (expressed *within* the systems, not forming part of the rules *of* the system) such as "Do not use a class unless it is a subclass of one which has been mentioned by teacher" can have a similar effect to "Do not go too near the edge."

The imperatives that can be obeyed by a machine that has no limbs are bound to be of a rather intellectual character, as in the example (doing homework) given above. Important among such imperatives will be ones which regulate the order in which the rules of the logical system concerned are to be applied. For at each stage when one is using a logical system, there is a very large number of alternative steps, any of which one is permitted to apply, so far as obedience to the rules of the logical system is concerned. These choices make the difference between a brilliant and a footling reasoner, not the difference between a sound and a fallacious one. Propositions leading to imperatives of this kind might be "When Socrates is mentioned, use the syllogism in Barbara" or "If one method has been proved to be quicker than another, do not use the slower method." Some of these may be "given by authority," but others may be produced by the machine itself, e.g., by scientific induction.

The idea of a learning machine may appear paradoxical to some readers. How can the rules of operation of the machine change? They should describe completely how the machine will react whatever its history might be, whatever changes it might undergo. The rules are thus quite time-invariant. This is quite true. The explanation of the paradox is that the rules which get changed in the learning process are of a rather less pretentious kind, claiming only an ephemeral validity. The reader may draw a parallel with the Constitution of the United States.

An important feature of a learning machine is that its teacher will often be very largely ignorant of quite what is going on inside, although he may still be able to some extent to predict his pupil's behavior. This should apply most strongly to the later education of a machine arising from a child-machine of well-tried design (or program). This is in clear contrast with normal procedure when using a machine to do computations: one's object is then to have a clear mental picture of the state of the machine at each moment in the computation. This object can only be achieved with a struggle. The view that "the machine can only do what we know how to order it to do,"[3] appears strange in face of this. Most of the programs which we can put into the machine will result in its doing something that we cannot make sense of at all, or which we regard as completely random

---

[3] Compare Lady Lovelace's statement, which does not contain the word "only."

behavior. Intelligent behavior presumably consists in a departure from the completely disciplined behavior involved in computation, but a rather slight one, which does not give rise to random behavior, or to pointless repetitive loops. Another important result of preparing our machine for its part in the imitation game by a process of teaching and learning is that "human fallibility" is likely to be omitted in a rather natural way, i.e., without special "coaching." Processes that are learned do not produce a hundred per cent certainty of result; if they did they could not be un-learned.

It is probably wise to include a random element in a learning machine. A random element is rather useful when we are searching for a solution of some problem. Suppose for instance we wanted to find a number between 50 and 200 which was equal to the square of the sum of its digits, we might start at 51 then try 52 and go on until we got a number that worked. Alternatively we might choose numbers at random until we got a good one. This method has the advantage that it is unnecessary to keep track of the values that have been tried, but the disadvantage that one may try the same one twice, but this is not very important if there are several solutions. The systematic method has the disadvantage that there may be an enormous block without any solutions in the region which has to be investigated first. Now the learning process may be regarded as a search for a form of behavior which will satisfy the teacher (or some other criterion). Since there is probably a very large number of satisfactory solutions the random method seems to be better than the systematic. It should be noticed that it is used in the analogous process of evolution. But there the systematic method is not possible. How could one keep track of the different genetical combinations that had been tried, so as to avoid trying them again?

We may hope that machines will eventually compete with men in all purely intellectual fields. But which are the best ones to start with? Even this is a difficult decision. Many people think that a very abstract activity, like the playing of chess, would be best. It can also be maintained that it is best to provide the machine with the best sense organs that money can buy, and then teach it to understand and speak English. This process could follow the normal teaching of a child. Things would be pointed out and named, etc. Again I do not know what the right answer is, but I think both approaches should be tried.

We can only see a short distance ahead, but we can see plenty there that needs to be done.

HARLOW SHAPLEY

The Fourth Adjustment

Harlow Shapley, one of the United States' most distinguished astronomers, is a professor at Harvard University. The problem of life elsewhere in the
universe has stimulated many scientists recently, and most have reached conclusions similar to Shapley's. Several projects have already been begun to listen
for intelligible radio signals from remote planets, and a logician has developed a
language (Lincos) particularly designed for communicating with intelligent entities
in other parts of the universe.

In the past history of the evolving human mind, with its increasing knowledge of the surrounding world, there must have been a
time when the philosophers of the early tribes began to realize that the
world is not simply anthropocentric, centered on man himself. As society
developed, the village attained central significance — a natural view supported first by the evidence of a circular horizon and second by the
increasing vagueness of the world as one increases the distance from
home. But the higher civilizations of the Near and Middle East (and
perhaps elsewhere) became increasingly conscious, a few thousand years
ago, of the daily revolving sun, stars, and wandering planets. The naviga-
tors detected evidence of the curvature of the surface of the oceans and of
the earth. The sphericity indicated thereby led to the belief that the center
of the earth rather than a locality on the surface was the center of the
visible universe. This view was thought to be consistent with the apparent
motions of the moon, planets, sun, and stars. The *geocentric* concept thus
became the common doctrine in many of the most civilized nations. It is
often labeled the Ptolemaic theory.

This first adjustment of man to the material universe was only mildly
disturbing to his self-conscious ego, for man appeared, on pretty good
evidence, to surpass all other living forms. He saw little reason, therefore,
to be openly humble. He personally was not central in the universe, but
his earth seemed to have that distinction.

From Geocentric to Heliocentric

The second adjustment was the abandonment of this earth-
center theory. The new hypothesis was not generally acceptable in the

Western world until the Copernican Revolution of the sixteenth century
soundly established the heliocentric concept. The liberal philosophers
and eventually the church fathers yielded to the scientists' theory of a
universe centered on our sun. It was a slow shift, for man is a stubborn
adherent to official dogma. In time, however, he accepted the sun as the
center not only of the local family of planets but also of the total sidereal
assemblage; and he long held that view. But it, too, was a fallacy. Another
shift was in the making as soon as the sun was recognized as an ordinary
star; but not until modern telescopes reported on globular star clusters,
galaxies, and cepheid variables did this further adjustment become
imperative.

The earth-centered cosmology had been given up, in favor of the sun-
centered theory, very reluctantly. And likewise, later, in spite of increasing evidence requiring a further change, the scientists, philosophers,
and laymen held doggedly to the heliocentric view. Was this because of
vanity — because of the feeling, cultivated by the unscientific dogmatists,
that man is of paramount significance in the world of stars and space-
time?

From Heliocentric to Sagittarius and Beyond

There are several better reasons for this erroneous concept
—for this heliocentric theory; they are quasi-scientific explanations of
what can be observed. For example, the Milky Way lies along a great
circle: it is a band of star-composed light that divides the sky into two
practically equal parts. Also, it is of about the same brightness in all parts.
By implication, therefore, the sun and earth are centrally located. A second evidence is that the numbers of stars seemed to the early census-
takers to fall off with distance from the sun in all directions as though it
were central; and such a position for his star among the stellar millions
brought a man a dignity of location that was not at all disagreeable. But
again it was an illusion.

As late as 1917 the leaders in astronomical interpretation held that the
sun was central, or at least very near the center of the sidereal universe.
(The galaxies were then not recognized officially as other great stellar
systems.) The introduction of the period-luminosity relation for cepheid
variable stars as a sounding tool, and the determination of the distances
and distribution in space of the globular star clusters, first indicated the
eccentric position of the earth, sun, and surrounding stars in the flattened
stellar system — in the stellar discoid made manifest by the star-crowded
Milky Way.

Gradually came other probing evidences that the billion-starred nucleus
of our spiral galaxy is remotely distant through the southern constellations
of Sagittarius, Ophiuchus, and Scorpio. Suffering from these new thrusts

into the stellar depths, the heliocentric theory of the stellar universe struggled briefly, weakened and died.

The center of the galaxy is not near at hand among the bright stars that define those southern constellations for they are but a few hundred light years away. The center of our galaxy, we have found, is more than twenty-five thousand light years distant. The billions of stars in that nucleus together make the extended white glow in the southern Milky Way which we call the great Sagittarius star cloud.

The shift from the geocentric to the heliocentric concept doubtless had some philosophical impact in the sixteenth century, but not a great deal. The hot, turbulent, gaseous sun would be no place for the delicate array of biological forms in which man finds himself at or near the top. Earth-center or sun-center seemed to make little difference to cosmic thinking. From the death bed of Copernicus to the birth of this century and later the prevailing heliocentric concept of the stellar universe incited little if any philosophical uneasiness.

But then, with the rapidly increasing accumulation of astronomical information, came the inescapable need for this third adjustment — one that should have deeply affected and to some extent has disturbed man's concern about his place, his career, and his destiny.

The shift of the sun and earth to the edge of our galaxy has considerably eroded human pride and self-assurance; it has carried with it the revelation of the appalling number of comparable galaxies. We could accept rather cheerfully the Darwinian evidence and argument for our animal origin (even though the theologians of a century ago found it strong medicine), for that evidence still left us, we believed, at the summit of all terrestrial organisms. But the abandonment of the heliocentric universe, on the basis of dependable astronomical evidence, was certainly deflationary from the standpoint of man's position in the material world, however flattering such advances of human knowledge were to the human mind.

The "galactocentric" hypothesis puts the earth and its life on the outer fringe of one galaxy in a universe of millions of galaxies. Man becomes peripheral among the billions of stars of his own Milky Way; and according to the revelations of paleontology and geochemistry, he is also exposed as a recent and probably ephemeral manifestation in the unrolling of cosmic time.

At this point we pause for a sombre or happy thought, one that is sombre or happy depending on one's mood. With the advance of science, and with the retreat of superstition and belief in the supernatural, we have in recent centuries gone so far and so firmly in our orientation of man in the universe that there is now no successful retreat! The inquiring human mind has passed the point of no return. We cannot restore geocentrism or even heliocentrism.

The apes, eagles, and honey bees, with their specialized skills and wisdoms, may be wholly content to be only peripheral ephemerals, and thus miss the great visions that open before us. For them egocentrism and lococentrism may suffice; for us, no! And since we cannot (and would not) go back to the cramped but comfortable past without sacrificing completely our cultures and civilizations, we go forward; and then we find that there is another chapter to the story of orientation. Geocentrism was not sufficient; nor is heliocentrism.

Another shift must be made, for we are concerned in this discussion not only with the location of our earth in the time and space of the physical world, but with our location in the world of biological phenomena.

The downgrading of the earth and sun and the elevation of the galaxies is not the end of our progress as scientific pilgrims, plodding through philosophical fields. As intimated on previous pages, the need for a further jolting adjustment now arises above the mental horizon. It is neither wholly unexpected by workers in scientific fields, or wholly the result of one or two scientific discoveries. It is a product of the age. We turn from astronomy to the overlap of a dozen other sciences and ask about the spread of life throughout the universe. As unsolicited spokesman for all earthly organisms of land, sea, and air I ask the piquant question: "In this universe of stars, space, and time, *are we alone?*"

Biological Orientation

From among the many thoughts and measures that promote this Fourth Adjustment of Homo sapiens in the galaxy of galaxies, three phenomena stand out as most meriting our further consideration. The first refers to the number of stars, the second to catastrophes of ancient days, and the third to the origin of self-replicating molecules. They are worth brief summarizing at this point. . . .

To the ancients only a few thousand stars were known; to the early telescopes, however, a million; and that astounding number has increased spectacularly with every telescopic advance. Finally, with the discovery that the so-called extra-galactic nebulae are in fact galaxies, each with its hundreds or even thousands of millions of stars, and with the inability to touch "metagalactic bottom" with the greatest telescopes, we are led to accept the existence of more than 10^{20} stars in our explorable universe, perhaps many more.

(The numbers of stars and their ages are of course not humanly comprehensible in the usual number terms — too many stars, too much space, too many years for our minds, which are accustomed to operate in serially countable numbers. The Macrocosmos transcends our counting. And comprehension is not simplified when we turn to the atomic Microcosmos and point out that in our next breath we shall each inhale more than 1000 million million million atoms [10^{21}], of oxygen, nitrogen, and argon.)

The second phenomenon, the expanding Metagalaxy, bears on the question: Do planets accompany at least some of the stars that radiate energy suitable for the complex biological activity that we call life?

We now accept the strong observational evidence of a universal redward shift in the light received from distant external galaxies, and accept also the interpretation of that red-shift as a result of the scattering and diffusion of galaxies and the expansion of the universe. The speed of the mutual recessions is about 20 miles a second for galaxies separated by a million light years; twice as fast for galaxies at twice the distance apart; three times at thrice the distance, and so on. The exact numerical values are still under investigation and revision, as is the possible failure to maintain at a very great separation this increase of scattering speed with distance.

The Turbulence of Long Ago

The present rapid dissipation of the Metagalaxy in all directions naturally turns thought to the situation of a year ago when the galaxies were closer together, and to a century, a millennium, a billion years ago. There was, of course, as we go back in time, an increasingly greater concentration of the now spreading cosmic units (galaxies). The average density of matter in space at present is very low — something like 10^{-30} grams per cubic centimeter, which by terrestrial standards is a veritable super-super-vacuum. A few thousand million years ago, however, the average density in the unexpanded universe must have been so great that collisions of stars and gravitational disruptions of planets, stars, and nebulae were inevitably frequent.

At that time countless millions of other planetary systems must have developed, for our sun is of a very common stellar type. Stars of non-solar types must have also participated in the cosmic turmoil.

Now here is an important coincidence. The crust of the earth, radioactively measured, is also a few thousand years old. Therefore the earth and the other planets of this planetary system were born in those crowded days of turbulence and disastrous encounters.

(Our sun, an ancient compared with many blue and red giants, is so ordinary that in Miss Cannon's famous spectrum catalogue we find some 40,000 sun-like stars, all in our immediate neighborhood.)

Other ways in which planets may be formed, other than by this slam-bang process of the earliest and most crowded times, have been proposed by astronomers and other scientists. For example, the gravitational contraction of proto-stars out of the hypothetical primeval gas and dust, giving birth to the proto-planets on the way, is an evolutionary process now widely favored. It would imply the existence of countless planets.

The head-on collision theory of planetary origin has been favorably considered in various versions. But the stars are now so widely dispersed that collisions must be exceedingly rare — so very unlikely, in fact, that we might claim uniqueness throughout all creation for ourselves if planet birth depended only upon collisional procedure, such as could now occur. But that vanity of uniqueness cannot be easily maintained, since the expanding universe discovery has shown the crowded conditions when our earth emerged out of chaos.

Passing over details, we again state the relevant conclusion: *Millions of planetary systems must exist,* and *billions* is the better word. Whatever the methods of origin, and doubtless more than one type of genesis has operated, planets may be the common heritage of all stars except those so situated that planetary materials would be swallowed up by greater masses or cast off through gravitational action.

In passing, we recall that astrophysics has shown that our kind of chemistry and physics prevails throughout the explorable universe. There is nothing uncommon and special here or now.

Remembering our 10^{20} stars and the high probability of millions of planets with suitable chemistry, dimensions, and distance from their nutrient stars, we are ready for the question: On some of these planets is there actually life? Or is that biochemical operation strangely limited to our planet — limited, that is, to No. 3 in the family of the sun, which is an average star located in the outer part of a galaxy that contains 100,000 million other stars — and this local galaxy but one of millions of galaxies already on the records?

Is life thus restricted? Of course not. We are not alone. And we can accept life's wide dispersion more confidently when our third observation is indicated.

To summarize in four sentences: Biochemistry and microbiology, with the assistance of geophysics, astronomy, and other sciences, have gone so far in bridging the gap between the inanimate and the living that we can no longer doubt that whenever the physics, chemistry, and climatology are right on a planet's surface, life will emerge, persist, and evolve. The mystery of life is vanishing. Objective science is replacing the subjective miraculous. The many researches in the past few years in the field of macromolecules and microorganisms have now made it quite unnecessary to postulate miracles and the supernatural for the origin of life. We must adjust our world view to the wide spread of life.

The step in human orientation that I call the Fourth Adjustment is ready for the taking, if we care to explore that opportunity. The scattering of galaxies, the abundance of stars, and the structure and habits of macromolecules on warm, moist, starlit planetary surfaces have prompted this further and most important adjustment in the understanding of the place and functioning of life in the universe. The acceptance of the evidence and argument that the biological development on this planet is not unique and that varied and highly elaborated sentient life is abundant and widely distributed has led to this most important step of all in the orientation of Homo in the material world.

Have we come now to the end of the journey, or are there other steps ahead? In view of the rapid growth of scientific techniques and the continual exercise of the human imagination, it would not be wise to suggest that we shall *never never* find need for a further adjustment in our knowledge of man's place in the universe — that we shall never discover a reason for an orientating adjustment that transcends both the physical and biological orientations which are now represented, respectively, by the third and fourth adjustments.

A fifth adjustment might be in the psychological realm, or in the "negative matter" world, or in one of those fanciful existences where our Metagalaxy is only an atom in some superuniverse, or in the equally droll (and equally possible) existence where our electrons are the galaxies in some microcosmic universe that is below our measures and our knowing.

STUDY AIDS

Study Aids

FRANK: Contemporary Science and the Contemporary World View

1. Throughout his essay Frank uses the phrase "common-sense language." What does he mean by that phrase? What difficulties might one encounter if one attempted to distinguish "common-sense language" from the language scientists use to define "general principles"? *Is* there a single, easily recognized language or mode of discourse for what Frank calls "common-sense"? Does Frank use "common-sense language" in this essay?

2. What is the most important thing contemporary science has to offer us, according to Frank? Is it a body of knowledge or a technique of analysis? If what he says is true, how might training in contemporary science benefit students of language and philosophy?

3. How does Frank defend science against the charge that it deals only in "dehumanized and dehydrated abstractions?" What do the scientist and the poet have in common, according to his view? Does the fact that they share a common activity of mind mean that they can easily communicate with each other?

FEYNMAN: Scientific Imagination

1. How does scientific imagination differ from imagination outside the sciences? Do you agree with Feynman that contemporary physics makes more demands on the imagination than previous ideas did?

2. Feynman suggests a distinction between symbols and objects. Can you ever treat objects without symbols?

3. Do you find it strange that a physics textbook is raising aesthetic considerations? In what sense can science be said to be beautiful?

WHORF: Science and Linguistics

1. Explain Whorf's concept of "natural logic."

2. The basic thesis of this paper is commonly called the "Whorfian Hy-

pothesis." What *is* this thesis? How could we go about demonstrating its truth or falsity?

3. How does the noun-verb distinction in the English language affect our common-sense view of the world?

4. If, as Whorf suggests, we use clocks in the physics of intensity, are we developing a physics without the time-concept, or are we only calling time by a different name?

BRIDGMAN: Word, Meanings, and Verbal Analysis

1. What limitations does Bridgman see as inherent in the nature of language? Why do we need language?

2. What is the relation between language and "pointing"? How would you describe a "pointing" definition of a term? How can you use "pointing" to assign a meaning to a term?

3. Bridgman mentions "operational" anlysis at one point, indicating that he has written extensively on it before. The discusson of length is an example of such an analysis. How does this kind of analysis differ from the usual "definition" of a word, such as the kind you find in a dictionary?

4. What advantage is there to "a verbal approach to abstraction"?

TOULMIN: Scientific Theories and Scientific Myths

1. What is a myth? Does Toulmin define myth? Can you determine his meaning from the contexts in which it is used? Are these meanings consistent with your previous conception of myth?

2. What is a "scientific question"? How is it distinguished from other kinds of questions?

3. How is one to tell if a scientific theory is used as a myth? Is Toulmin consistent on this, or does he offer several independent criteria?

CLIFFORD: On the Aims and Instruments of Scientific Thought

1. Distinguish carefully between Clifford's two meanings for the word "exact" as applied to scientific theory. Why does he consider one to be untenable?

2. Does Clifford's use of "explanation" correspond to that in the everyday language? Should it? He mentions that different views of "explanation" in science are held by different scientists. Could one establish a reasonable criterion to distinguish between these different views? Why is Clifford interested in the pleasure generated by an explanation?

3. Clifford calls energy "a technical term out of mathematical physics". Is energy a "term" or a "thing"? Is energy also a term in everyday English? Why is Clifford insisting that it is a technical term?

SCHRÖDINGER: The Law of Chance

1. Give some examples from everyday situations of cause-effect relationships other than those mentioned in the article. Why do you consider these as cause and effect? What kinds of entities can be "causes"? Is "cause" only "a word"? Does it relate to something which is not a word?

2. Elucidate Schrödinger's statement that "chance lies at the root of causality". Does it seem paradoxical that random behavior can lead to causal behavior?

3. Are Schrödinger's two alternative views of causality at the end of the article intrinsically different? In what sense can he say that the first alternative is "revolutionary"? What might persuade us to accept this alternative? Does Schrödinger suggest which of the alternatives he favors?

TURING: Computing Machinery and Intelligence

1. What is the problem discussed in the article? Why does Turing think that defining terms is a useless way to study the problem? Compare his method with Bridgman's. When is a question "meaningless"?

2. Consult other sources to see if Turing's predictions for 2000 are already near realization. What is the capacity of present-day digital computers? How fast do they work? What can they do?

3. What is a learning machine? Why is this concept useful to Turing in developing his general argument?

SHAPLEY: The Fourth Adjustment

1. In what sense does man's location in the physical universe parallel his "location" in the biological world? Is this only loose use of the word "location" in two different ways?

2. Shapley claims that there are more than 10^{20} suns. What does "10^{20}" mean? What does 10^{-30} grams per cubic centimeter mean? Why is it useful to use a special linguistic device to indicate a large number? Is it permissible to use a mathematical expression as part of an English sentence? Are there any limitations to this?

3. Review the stages of the argument showing that "we are not alone". Where is the argument based on experimental information? Where do considerations of probability enter? Where do relevant scientific theories enter? How would you go about determining if the argument is "good"?

4. If it were conclusively established that intelligent living entities are present in many parts of the universe, would this affect any of your present attitudes concerning yourself? Explain your answer.

1 2 3 4 5 6 7 8 9 0